SERIOUS MEN~ ~
A Famil

Gwen Howe is a retired men
three previous books on seriou
She has been an active member
nia Fellowship for the past
member of Depression Alliance's professional advisory
panel and Co-ordinator of a local pressure group of sufferers
and carers.

Overcoming Common Problems Series

For a full list of titles please contact
Sheldon Press, Marylebone Road, London NW1 4DU

Overcoming Common Problems

SERIOUS MENTAL ILLNESS
A Family Affair

Gwen Howe

•

sheldonPRESS

First published in Great Britain in 1997 by
Sheldon Press, SPCK, Marylebone Road, London NW1 4DU

British Library Cataloguing-in-Publication Data
A catalogue record for this book is available from the British Library

ISBN 0 85969–752–5

Photoset by Deltatype Ltd, Birkenhead, Merseyside
Printed in Great Britain by Biddles Ltd, Guildford

Contents

This book is for Doris, Ena, Mary, Molly, Rita, Sandy, and, of course, my good friend, Sally Alsford

Acknowledgements

I am indebted to Tina Taylor, friend and fellow campaigner and member of The Manic Depression Fellowship's Council of Management. She read the drafts of nine chapters of this book and offered ideas and constructive criticism, most of which have been taken on board and, I believe, have greatly improved the value of the finished work.

I am also indebted, too, to friends for letting me use their (well disguised) experiences as sufferers and carers in the hope that these will help others to understand what it means to live with a serious mental illness.

My heartfelt thanks to my daughter, Sally Cooper, for once again reading manuscripts and offering the occasional inspired comment, together with much needed encouragement when my confidence and enthusiasm flaged.

Finally, a thank you to my publisher, Joanna Moriarty, for suggesting the theme of this book, and to Mary Ellen Copeland, whose successful pioneering of a self-management approach has made this a pleasure to write, as well as providing light at the end of the tunnel!

Introduction

Individuals with conditions such as manic depression or schizophrenia can lose touch with reality at the time of breakdown. Most of us are aware of this and associate such illnesses with disturbing media headlines and with violence. However, this is a tragically distorted picture as the vast majority of sufferers – around half a million of them in the UK – are *not* violent; they are law-abiding, often sensitive, people trying to get on with their lives despite the problems and social stigma associated with their diagnosis.

This book seeks to explain what serious mental illness is all about and how its victims are frequently talented and particularly creative individuals. Indeed, the world has been enriched by the heritage of paintings, poems and music left by artists who had to cope with manic depression or schizophrenia. Sadly, though, while sufferers can, and do, live normal lives, far too many are needlessly damaged by delays in diagnosis and treatment because the system generally responds to full-blown crisis situations rather than to early signs of a developing illness or a threatened relapse.

Because of the stigma and ignorance associated with these types of illness, many very able and fit sufferers feel the need to hide their illness. At least one of your friends, neighbours or colleagues at work probably has a manic depressive illness or schizophrenia unbeknown to you. The subject is surrounded by secrecy and yet these conditions are so common that around two in every one hundred of the population will have such a diagnosis during their lifetime.

I write about this subject because I have long been convinced that we can stop most of the damage and waste of lives associated with serious mental illness just by taking a preventive approach instead of waiting for crisis after crisis to erupt. Unfortunately, there has been no sign of this happening. The care and treatment of individuals with a serious mental illness have taken second place to political expediency and misplaced ideology for the past three decades. It is therefore a joy to report that while I have been writing this book, there has been a determined move by sufferers themselves to push ahead with self-management pro-grammes, which are all about preventing breakdowns and keeping well. At last there now seems to be some hope for the future.
Gwen Howe, June 1996

Part I Coping with breakdown

1

About serious mental illness

The reality is that one in every five of the population is treated at some time for a psychiatric illness, and two in every hundred of us will contract schizophrenia or manic depression (MD) during our lifetime. Schizophrenia and MD are what we call psychotic illnesses – those conditions that can cause sufferers to lose touch with reality at times of breakdown. This can put them very much at risk and this is why we refer to this type of illness as being *serious* although, much of the time, sufferers may be well and live reasonably normal lives.

Few of us know much about psychosis, or serious mental illness, unless we experience it, either as something that happens to us or to someone close to us. Because it tends to be something that no one talks about, the whole subject is submerged in ignorance and fear. Newspaper headlines and top-selling novels on the subject tend to be full of horror stories that in no way reflect the everyday lives of the vast majority who have had suffered from psychosis. Instead, they just add to the stress and suffering of coping with what is a really very common type of illness.

Although serious mental illness is very much part of the 'human condition', it sometimes seems that it is, nevertheless, the final taboo in our society. So much so, that some of the professionals who work with psychosis tend to avoid mentioning it or worse, deny it. Sadly, it is this secrecy and denial that causes so much unnecessary pain for sufferers and those who love them.

So, what can be done about the ignorance and fear that springs from the secrecy and denial which surrounds this subject?

Sharing information

Well, we can start by offering ordinary families basic and straightforward information that should enable them to appreciate what is happening if a relative develops a serious mental illness. In turn, this knowledge should lead to a better understanding of what happens in this sort of illness. It should also lead to an appreciation of what helps and what doesn't help the sufferer, rather than having to stumble along, learning by trial and error. Ideally, informed families can then approach professionals with some confidence and understanding of the system and perhaps even persuade experts that a well-informed sufferer and

5

family can be a real bonus for the hard-pressed mental health services. Most important of all, well-informed relatives have a greater chance than others of coping with what has happened and of staying together instead of letting the illness destroy the family unit, which most of us need so much more when we are vulnerable.

This book is about sharing information in this way. Let's start with a brief discussion about what it can mean to suffer from a psychotic illness.

What is psychosis?

By psychosis, we are referring to what used to be called madness in the bad old days before effective treatment was available. If and when sufferers lose touch with reality, the first thing that happens is that they become convinced that their problems are not caused by an illness.

There is perhaps one thing we all know about 'madness', as it used to be called: if a friend says 'I think I'm going mad', we say something like 'don't worry, if you were really going mad you wouldn't know you were'. And we would be right! This one truism we all seem to know sums up the dangers of a psychotic episode; sufferers don't recognise what is happening. It is from this point on that they become very much at risk and vulnerable, embroiled in a confusing world of their own and acting in a way that makes little sense to the onlooker. Let's take a closer look at the two most common types of psychotic illness.

Manic depression (MD)

Another medical term for this condition is *bipolar affective disorder*, 'affective' being another word for mood. This illness is all about mood swings and when individuals are given this diagnosis, it means that they have experienced extreme highs and lows, that is they have, at some time, suffered at least one episode of mania and a clinical depression.

Most of us suffer from swings of mood. We have days when everything seems right and days when we seem to 'have got out of bed the wrong side' and everything seems bleak and grey. To suffer from MD is to experience *excessive* swings of mood, to the extent that the low periods can be truly bleak. They have been described by sufferers as 'like being enveloped by a dark cloud'. Equally, the 'highs' can be brilliant and colourful before leading into euphoria, mental confusion and delusions. The individual may feel all-powerful, capable of achieving anything. For most sufferers, much of a 'high' can be exciting and stimulating – initially anyway – but it can also be very disruptive to their everyday lives. A 'low' period can be full of darkness, with distorted, pessimistic thoughts and the kind of despair that sometimes leads to suicidal ideas.

Sadly, an unfortunate minority of individuals diagnosed as having MD suffer continuously, ever yo-yoing from mania to deep depression, hardly pausing in normality between these two extremes. More usually, though, MD sufferers can lead reasonably stable lives for much of the time, although their everyday lives may be overshadowed by a tendency to depression or unnatural highs. More importantly, most have to live with the knowledge that they are vulnerable to further relapses.

On the whole, the prognosis for MD can be a good one and, with care, many can get on with their lives and enjoy a rewarding lifestyle. Jan fits into this group.

Jan

A couple of years into an ideally happy marriage, Jan was referred to a psychiatrist as she had become weepy and distressed about her job. She was treated with antidepressants and became less depressed, but three months later, she was still off work and becoming frantically involved with all sorts of projects that were going to change the world – help various oppressed groups, as she saw them. To her husband's dismay, the house was suddenly overflowing with enormous amounts of knitting wool and greetings cards and tools for the work she was taking on for her new and various 'causes'. These were mostly concerned with charities and the Church, and she talked about religion much of the time, although this had not previously played a prominent role in her life. When she wasn't at church, involving others in her plans, she was frantically fundraising and, despite usually showing a sensible and cautious approach to life, she was also spending money in an alarming manner.

This pattern escalated to the point where Jan was totally absorbed in her projects, had started the process of buying a new home, unbeknown to her husband, and had not slept for several nights. At this point, she was convinced she was Jesus Christ and that her mission was to save the world. She was never still for more than a few minutes at a time and was organising everyone around her, with some very real success as others found it difficult to resist her expectations of them and her confident enthusiasm was infectious.

However, things were rapidly getting out of control and Jan was eventually admitted to hospital and was really quite ill for the next 18 months, although most of this time was spent at home. She'd yo-yo between mania and deep depression while doctors struggled to find the right balance of drugs to help her. When elated, her behaviour was similar to that at the point of her breakdown, although less extreme now she was under medical supervision. When depressed, she fled to her bed and resisted all attempts to move her from it.

Jan's illness was so prolonged that her husband was despairing of her ever being well again. She now believes it was worse for him than for her, as she was either intensely involved in exciting ventures or 'switched off' and not wanting anything but her bed and the release of sleep.

All this was eight years ago. Thankfully, she is now well, happy with her work (her original responsible job was kept open for her) and keenly involved with her husband in helping others to find that they, too, can survive a serious mental illness.

As well as taking sensible precautions with her health, Jan is careful to take the prescribed balance of medication, which eventually brought her nightmare to an end. Her good health and busy lifestyle are testimony to the wisdom of this approach to her illness.

Schizophrenia

Schizophrenia is a word that may describe a group of conditions that has a cluster of symptoms in common, rather than just one illness. However, at present, we have no choice but to use this cumbersome and fearsome name and refer to just two divisions; *acute* and *chronic schizophrenia*.

The acute illness is made up of various bizarre experiences we associate with a psychotic breakdown, with sufferers 'hearing voices' and believing all sorts of impossible things are happening or about to happen. These symptoms respond to medication and are usually of a temporary nature.

Quite differently, the chronic illness deprives sufferers of social skills the rest of us use in our everyday interactions with others. It also has many of the features of a depressive illness, such as withdrawal and a severe lack of energy and motivtion.

The symptoms of these two types schizophrenia are so different that we might be tempted to think of them as two different conditions, but we are confounded in this because 'acute' sufferers can slip into the chronic illness and 'chronic' sufferers can have an acute breakdown. Similarly, a sufferer can, at any one time, experience some of the symptoms of both types of condition.

Some individuals who have the acute form of illness may have just one or two psychotic episodes. Others will have more frequent and intermittent breakdowns. Importantly, each one of these breakdowns brings with it the risk of lapsing into the chronic form of schizophrenia, involving seemingly irreversible changes in personality and lifestyle.

At worst, around 10 per cent of all schizophrenia sufferers will be in need of continuous institutional care, while at the other end of the continuum, around 25 per cent will have no more than a single breakdown, even though they may not remain completely free of symptoms. In between these two extremes, the illness will usually have quite a serious effect on the lives of at least half of the remaining 65 per cent of sufferers. Harry is one of the less fortunate in this large group.

Harry

Harry's first attack of schizophrenia, at the age of 16, was treated as an 'adolescent crisis' and he was discharged after a few weeks without ongoing treatment. Sadly, his panic attacks were not recognised for what they were – the result of confused messages reaching his brain and the start of a schizophrenic illness. He was struggling to survive in a world that had become strange and menacing.

Ten months later, Harry suffered a severe breakdown. This time, the doctors diagnosed the underlying illness which had led to his earlier admission to hospital. However, the young man was now very seriously ill and, despite many months of treatment in hospital, he was a shadow of his original self when discharged. The illness had started to take its toll.

After three years, he was beginning to enjoy some quality of life again and was starting to fulfil some of the potential he had been showing at school before he first became ill, but progress was slow and he remained vulnerable. A change in his domestic life around the same time that a doctor decided to reduce Harry's medication led to a second major breakdown.

It took many months before he recovered enough to return to the community, now more seriously damaged than before. Harry then had to face a further long struggle back to more normal health. Although he had the courage to take up this challenge, he has never reached the potential he was showing just before his last illness and no longer expects to be able to eventually hold down a job and have what he considers to be a normal lifestyle.

Anne is another individual in this 65 per cent of sufferers for whom prognosis is always difficult to predict.

Anne

Anne suffered several breakdowns during her late teens. Because no one explained to her or her family the cause of these breakdowns, she quickly came off her medication each time she believed she was well again and then relapsed shortly afterwards.

This happened three times before Anne and her family were made aware of her diagnosis and why she should continue to take the medication (we will look at this subject further in Chapter 3). From this point on, she started to make real progress. A couple of threatened relapses were arrested by adjusting her medication and a few days' 'sanctuary' in hospital, and she has now remained stable for over five years, becoming increasingly well and enjoying a completely normal lifestyle.

Although she occasionally has to cope with 'shadowy' symptoms and brief periods of doubt and anxiety, no one would know this capable and attractive young woman has suffered several bouts of an acute schizophrenic illness unless they were told.

MD and schizophrenia – similarities and differences

As we have seen, the common ground between MD and schizophrenia is that both are psychotic conditions that can loosen the sufferer's grip on reality. While schizophrenia is not an *affective* disorder – it is more concerned with altered perceptions of the outside world and delusional ideas than with excesses of mood – there are, nevertheless, a significant minority of individuals who seem to have both types of symptoms and some who may be diagnosed as having a 'schizo-affective disorder' (a mixture of both conditions). Also, it is not uncommon for an individual treated successfully for a typical schizophrenic illness to develop MD in later years.

Diagnosis – a hornet's nest!

As we have seen, it may not be easy to differentiate between MD and schizophrenia in a minority of cases, but this does not necessarily have to be a problem as the same treatment may be applicable to these overlapping conditions.

Although such similarities can sometimes cause delay in making a diagnosis, we have to look further for an explanation for the quite awesome delays that often take place before diagnosis and treatment are forthcoming for many sufferers. This is a serious matter as it is now known that a psychotic illness is no different to any other – the sooner it is treated, the better! This becomes even more serious when we bear in mind that most first episodes of schizophrenia are diagnosed in young people in their teens and early twenties, which is far too young, surely, to take risks with the rest of their lives. What, then, leads to unnecessary delays in diagnosis and treatment?

We have already referred to secrecy and denial about psychotic illness in some professionals who work in this area. There is, of course, a precedent for this. Fifty years ago, doctors did not talk about cancer, even to their patients, and, consequently, no one else talked about it either – it was clearly too awful to talk about! Thankfully, this has all changed now and everyone is more open and frank – and less scared – about this common group of diseases. Sadly, such a change has not happened regarding mental illness. Indeed, the secrecy and denial has actually *worsened* during the past few decades and the waters have become so muddied that health professionals talk about *labelling* sufferers rather than *diagnosing* them, the implication being that we shouldn't acknowledge their illness because of the stigma attached to it. Sadly, much energy and effort has been devoted to exposing the evils of giving someone a dreaded label rather than making a serious effort to do away with the stigma and ignorance surrounding a common diagnosis and getting on with treating the sufferer as promptly as possible.

A 'let's wait and see' policy

Such attitudes have influenced society's handling of serious mental illness and now we have a system that encourages a 'let's wait and see' approach to psychotic breakdown and, consequently, squanders most of its resources on responding to crisis situations rather than protecting sufferers from the ravages of an untreated psychosis. This is discussed further in Chapter 10, but suffice to say now that many families who seek help for a seriously mentally ill relative are baffled by the lack of response they receive and some even find that they meet the same sort of denial when a diagnosed sufferer shows signs of relapse at a later date.

Personality disorder – a real label

Before leaving this subject of trying to get into the system, it might be helpful for families to know that even while sufferers wait for a real diagnosis, they may well find themselves labelled as having a personality disorder instead.

A survey carried out by the Schizophrenia Association of Great Britain revealed that about a third of schizophrenia sufferers involved in a survey of members during the early 1980s had been given this label before a proper diagnosis was made. It is interesting that all those MD and schizophrenia sufferers I have known who have been given this

11

label have felt degraded and insulted by it. So much for ideas about protecting sufferers, particularly as, unlike a personality disorder both MD and schizophrenia are eminently treatable!

Over recent years, the use of the term personality disorder has brought with it more sinister undertones. The mental health legislation allows for compulsory admission to hospital for individuals with a personality disorder only if doctors consider they will benefit from treatment. As beds are becoming increasingly scarce, so the increasing use of this label puts sufferers at risk of being excluded under the mental health legislation.

We will come back to this vexing subject later, but, meanwhile, here is another good reason to press for a proper diagnosis of a treatable condition and, even more so, to ensure that once this has been achieved, it is not denied at a later date.

More about the incidence of serious mental illness

One very interesting fact about schizophrenia, the most common form of psychosis, is that it occurs in a markedly uniform way throughout the world. Furthermore, the same cluster of symptoms has been found in old tribal societies as is regularly found in industrialized societies. This means that schizophrenia is not related to any particular lifestyle and upbringing, as was claimed by the old 'family theories' in the 1960s and 1970s, nor are this illness and MD a product of our modern Western civilization.

One important difference between MD and schizophrenia is that, with the latter illness, 80 per cent of sufferers are first diagnosed between the ages of 16 and 25 years, whereas MD sufferers can become ill for the first time at any age from puberty to old age, with a significant number succumbing in their thirties. Also, in schizophrenia, the illness tends to appear earlier in males than in females and is often more disabling for male sufferers, though the reasons for this are not clear. However, in MD, although males tend to be more susceptible to contracting the illness where this runs in families, generally female sufferers outnumber males.

Importantly, neither MD nor schizophrenia respect wealth, class or fame. The rich and privileged are just as likely to have an incidence of psychosis within their family as the poor, although the progression of the illness may result in 'downward mobility' in more damaged sufferers, with some of these ending up living in deprived inner city areas in relative poverty.

Causes of serious mental illness

This has been the subject of considerable interest over many decades. There has been an ongoing academic debate that has largely been concerned with whether or not psychosis is caused by 'nature' or 'nurture' – that is, whether it is in the genes or to do with a person's upbringing – and this has led to claims that psychosis is learned behaviour rather than an illness. 'Family theories', which blamed the parents of sufferers for their family's distress, dominated in the 1960s and 1970s, but these were poorly researched and have now been entirely discredited. However, old ideas die hard in some of those professionals whose training focused on such theories and in others who perhaps find it reassuring to believe that conditions with so much stigma attached to them only happen to 'those' families.

Other ideas that have been mooted in this same debate include suggestions that psychotic illness is a product of an insane society or represents a subconscious escape from the miseries of an individual's day-to-day life – a release, in fact, from an unhappy world. Perhaps not surprisingly, I have yet to meet one individual who has to cope with a serious mental illness who sees this as a happy release from anything! In fact, the main flaw with all such theories has been that they have neither demonstrated an understanding of life with a serious mental illness nor contributed anything to easing this – indeed, quite the contrary in many cases.

On a more practical and serious note, there is increasing evidence that abnormalities in brain chemistry are involved in serious mental illness and that these can be inherited or result from damage such as that incurred in trauma to the brain before or during birth or as a result of later injury. Careful research into identical twins (these are twins who share exactly the same genes) has indicated that if one of them becomes schizophrenic, then the other has a 47 per cent chance of also becoming ill. This is nearly five times the risk a non-identical twin or any other brother or sister of a sufferer has of becoming ill themselves. Such findings are very interesting because they point conclusively to genes being involved in some cases of schizophrenia, but they also point to the fact that other, presently unknown, factors must be involved as, otherwise, the risks for identical twins would be equal.

It is now thought that around half of all cases of serious mental illness run in families. We don't yet understand why some members of these same families don't contract a psychotic illness, any more than we understand why many individuals develop such a condition where there are no signs of psychosis in their family history. It seems likely that it is a

13

predisposition to having this type of illness, rather than the illness itself, that is inherited and that the presence, or absence, of certain other, unknown factors will influence whether or not it materialises. We still have a lot to learn!

Two sides of one coin

Before going on to look at the symptoms and experiences of MD and schizophrenia sufferers, this might be a good time to pause for a moment to consider some of the pluses and minuses that seem to be associated with these conditions.

Sadly, fewer sufferers are likely to be gainfully employed than is normal throughout the population. They are also less likely to marry, and this applies particularly to male sufferers. Although females are more likely to marry, marriage breakdown is quite frequent. None of these sad statistics are very surprising considering that these illnesses may result in intermittent breakdowns, with hospital admissions and gradual deterioration for a considerable minority of sufferers.

Needless to say, there is nothing – other than a not uncommon prejudice and ignorance among employers – to stop well-recovered sufferers from pursuing a successful career and, similarly, having a good marriage. Many do both. Moreover, the old maxim that 'genius is next to madness' applies here when we consider the brilliant achievements of many of the world's best-loved artists, musicians and poets, some of whom have most certainly suffered from MD or schizophrenia.

Most professionals who have worked on a day-to-day basis with serious mental illness will confirm my own experience, which has been that a large group of sufferers have the potential to be very successful, particularly in a more tolerant and informed society. Some of the individuals I have met over the past 20 years have been endowed with exceptional creative gifts and others have won scholarships to Oxbridge or have had all the makings of becoming outstanding athletes before they developed their illness. Finally, many more show a dogged determination and courage in coping with adversity, which is quite humbling for those of us who may have been blessed with an easier path through life.

2

Some symptoms and experiences
of serious mental illness

Not only can there be an overlap in the diagnosis of MD and schizophrenia, but the two illnesses also have various symptoms in common, particularly during a psychotic episode. As this can all become rather confusing, let's first take a separate look at the typical symptoms of the two conditions that make up MD and then at the typical symptoms of the acute and chronic forms of schizophrenia. This will highlight the main differences between them before we then consider these together with any similarities.

Mania

There may be two stages in a manic phase. The first, milder one is described as *hypomania* and this can be experienced by sufferers as an exhilarating and euphoric period. Their enthusiasm and drive may be quite infectious and they often make attractive and exciting companions.

Unfortunately, this phase can escalate into *mania*, with increasing incoherence and loss of reality. Here are some of the symptoms and signs of the hypomanic and manic conditions.

A general speeding up

There is a general speeding up of movement and speech. The sufferer may be 'on the go' the whole time and literally bounce with energy and enthusiasm, making all sorts of plans, some quite inspired, but tending to become more and more irrational as the mania progresses.

A lack of sleep

This may be the first sign of things going wrong. Sufferers show little concern with a need to sleep; at most, an hour's nap may recharge their batteries and they may be up night after night busily occupied with all sorts of increasingly ambitious plans and, very possibly, a desire to involve everyone else in them.

Increased awareness and creativity

Sufferers speak of everything seeming to be larger than life, with colours and sounds having a new intensity and brightness. There is an increased awareness of everything around them and a euphoria that can lead to brilliant creativity in some individuals. It is easy to see why Gary resents his wife trying to restrain his rising mood when he knows that friends and acquaintances are seeking his company and he is turning out some of his finest painting. These are the times when he asks her stingingly if she would prefer him to be depressed and unproductive?

Overconfidence, an inflated self-esteem

Sufferers exhibit a marked sense of superiority with a potentially dangerous confidence in their own abilities and opinions.

Don's experience when manic may illustrate this. He became the greatest guitar player that ever lived, greater even than Eric Clapton, his hero. He spent money and time trying to launch himself on this brilliant new career. His overconfidence had reached the point of delusion (we will discuss this subject again later in this chapter).

Irritability and impatience

Feelings of superiority may contribute to sufferers being critical and dismissive of the opinions of others. They tend to be argumentative and impatient and are likely to become verbally abusive at any attempts to restrain their excitement. Those closest to them may find sufferers sharp and hostile at this time.

Lisa was convinced that her property speculation ideas were a certain way to make a fortune. The discussions with her husband on this led to physical blows, which were totally out of character for this normally loving couple.

Pressure of speech

Sufferers exhibit a marked need to share their enthusiasm, to talk incessantly about their plans and ideas, and they may well spend hours on the telephone, both day and night. This need to speak all the time may escalate to the point where the individual may talk incessantly at a truly incredible speed, often becoming quite incoherent.

Flight of ideas

Alongside the pressure of speech it is common to find that there is a pronounced inability in sufferers to follow through on one line of thought, and the listener may be baffled by constant changes of direction and ideas.

Loss of judgement

A distorted perception of what is happening leads to impulsive decision making, a lack of caution and an absence of any sense of danger. Jan lives in a busy town and she remembers with horror that when she was manic, she used to treat the road outside the hospital as if it was the pavement, with no concern whatever for the traffic rushing by. Such loss of judgement is probably the most worrying aspect of a manic breakdown.

A preoccupation with spending money

Another far-reaching and frustrating effect of a manic breakdown can be a frequent tendency for sufferers to spend money as if there were no tomorrow. Individuals and their families have been ruined financially by just one episode of illness.

The spending seems to be for its own sake rather than to obtain longed-for luxuries. Jack, a warm and generous man in his forties, actually managed to give away two cars in one afternoon (he had bought one of them earlier that day when he was meant to be safely in hospital). This episode was one too many for his wife. After years of struggling to cope with much of the same, she finally gave up on an otherwise good marriage.

Lack of inhibition

This, of course, features in much of the sort of behaviour described above and it can lead to an anguished consciousness of loss of dignity and pride after a manic episode. Even more seriously, this lack of inhibition can lead to an increase in sexual activity, even promiscuity, which may be entirely out of character and put the individual's future at risk. This was the case with Brenda, a 40-year-old personal assistant, who started wearing critically short mini-skirts, staying out at night and bringing her conquests back to her and her husband's home.

Psychosis

Finally, if the mania continues unabated, it can be expected to escalate into a psychosis featuring delusions and hallucinations (both of which are discussed later in this chapter). Let's now take a look at the symptoms of depression, which might be regarded as the 'flip side' of mania or the other end of a continuum of mood excesses.

Depression

A general slowing down

In stark contrast to the main features of mania, individuals suffering from depression can become so slowed down in their movements, speech and thinking, that they may seem to be retarded. Eric's case is typical. When he became depressed, it took him so long to answer a question – albeit usually only with a 'yes', or 'no' or 'I don't know' – that the other person had usually given up on receiving a reply by the time he spoke.

Altered sleeping and eating patterns

Although they may long to escape into unconsciousness, some sufferers get very little sleep, often waking up in the early hours. Others tend to sleep much more than is normal. Similarly, whereas many sufferers lose their appetite and any interest in food during a depression, some tend to eat a lot more than usual.

Impaired concentration and lack of staying power

The ability to concentrate becomes very impaired and this can affect sufferers' ability to complete even the most commonplace tasks, Ellen was mortified when she couldn't cope with everyday tasks like washing-up and, more often than not, gave up on preparing an evening meal for her husband. Worse, she believed she had permanently lost the ability to do such things.

A lack of energy and drive

Whereas in mania there is an *abundance* of energy and motivation, in depression there is a *lack* of energy and drive, which merely aggravates the sorts of difficulties with coping that Ellen experienced.

Feelings of hopelessness and inferiority

The optimism and overconfidence of mania is replaced by feelings of hopelessness and inferiority. The sufferer may lack the confidence and ability to make even the smallest decision.

Embarrassment and self-loathing

Distorted perceptions of one's own ability and value can lead to self-loathing, thus contributing to a common tendency to withdraw from others. A pronounced disregard for personal hygiene may be a feature of this self-loathing.

Feelings of guilt and worthlessness

Feelings of guilt may have no grounds in reality at all or they may be attached to past failings or perceived mistakes, memories of which became distorted. Sufferers complain that these sorts of negative and punishing thoughts go round and round in their head, incessantly tormenting them.

Increased inhibition

In contrast to the general lack of inhibition, including a tendency to promiscuous sexual activity noted in mania, in depression there is a loss of interest in sex and generally overinhibition resulting from a crippling anxiety.

Anxiety and agitation

Irrational anxiety, often amounting to pronounced agitation, is common in depression. This agitation can lead to anguished repetitive questions about the future and a need for constant reassurance. In some sufferers, the agitation can reach the stage of having panic attacks.

Thoughts of death

There may be a morbid preoccupation with thoughts of death and the making of suicidal plans, whether or not these are intended to be acted upon. Suicidal ideas are, anyway, quite common in depression. There is a real danger of attempted or actual suicide and those close to the individual should be alerted to this.

Psychosis

As with mania, but less commonly, a severe depression may reach the stage where it escalates into a psychosis featuring hallucinations and delusions.

Acute schizophrenia

We refer to the cluster of experiences that make up the psychotic phase of a schizophrenic illness as 'positive' symptoms because they add something to the individual's experience. These may be divided into three main groups, as follows.

1 Hallucinations

When sufferers have hallucinations, their perception of what is happening has altered. Any one, or all, of their five senses may be playing tricks on them. Let's look at some examples of how this may work in practice.

Hearing

Sufferers may hear vague sounds that are inaudible to others because they are happening in the sufferer's head (we don't yet understand the mechanics of this phenomenon). These may take the form of music or mutterings and whispering, but, more commonly, sufferers hear voices.

These can be frightening and very real in their intensity. They can also be dangerous as the voices may continuously shout out insults and abuse or, worse, instructions urging self-damage or damage to others. Jonathan jumped from an upstairs window, permanently injuring himself because a tormenting voice told him all would be well if he jumped. He and others stress that the voices are so real and overwhelming at such times that they temporarily cancel out any form of reasoning.

Before her first breakdown, Pat lived with another common type of voice – one that mimicked her father's. Even while he and her mother were asleep, she'd listen to this voice night after night plotting to kill her because, apparently, he considered Pat had harmed her mother in some way so she must die.

Carol North, an American who later became a psychiatrist, was tormented by another common phenomenon – *several* voices running a commentary on her every action, of the 'Look at her now, she's going to the door' variety. Frustrating and distracting enough in this form, the voices later became more sinister, urging her to jump off a roof and all would be well.

Sight

Much less common than the hearing of voices, alterations of visual perceptions tend to be experienced as flashing lights or seeing things in a distorted way. Don used to be terrified by the faces of those around him changing shape and becoming grotesque even as he glanced at them. Others have been unable to look in mirrors because their image becomes ugly and distorted. More unusually, Leonard shared his home on and off with a ghost for some years who would always return to his bedroom when Leonard was not so well. In between times, he could believe the ghost to be a figment of his imagination, but not when his guest returned.

Touch, taste and smell

Sufferers' sense of touch can play tricks on them, and they may describe handling an apparently smooth surface only to find it feels furry or putting their feet down on a level floor only to have it start moving. Rather differently and more upsettingly, they can experience someone or something touching them, although there is no explanation for this.

Taste can also be affected and sufferers may complain that their food seems to have no taste at all or, more frequently, that everything has started to taste 'bitter' or 'coppery' (these are the two words invariably used), particularly at times of breakdown.

Similarly, it is not uncommon for the sense of smell to be affected. Some individuals complain of putrid smells where there should be none.

Tim's family were made to feel rather uncomfortable by his demands that they should bath more! Others have been devastated by a consciousness of an 'evil smell' coming from their own bodies.

2 Delusions

Delusional ideas can best be described as fixations that are impervious to reasoned argument. The individual believes the impossible and nothing anyone else says on the subject makes any difference at all.

Having just looked at the sorts of tricks that their senses may be playing on them, we can perhaps begin to understand how sufferers' delusional ideas tie up with these false messages they receive; they even become predictable. Take, for example, the individual who has been trying to cope with a suddenly hostile world and then his food starts tasting 'bitter' or 'coppery' instead of the way it should taste. It is only a short step for him to decide that someone is doctoring his food or trying to poison him – and this is a very common delusion. Similarly, when Don's eyes used to play tricks on him, making the faces around him change shape, his brain needed to find an explanation for this phenomenon. He thus became convinced that some all-powerful evil force was changing and distorting everything in front of his eyes.

Paranoia

Our everyday use of this word does not explain the paranoia very commonly experienced as part of a psychotic illness as this is provoked by false messages reaching the individual's brain rather than by the actions of others. Tragically, this sort of paranoia inevitably focuses on those who matter most to the individual. Pat's paranoia about her father was fanned by false messages caused by her illness and by the mimicking in her head of his voice. His continuing love and concern for her could not intrude on this inner world.

Grandiose ideas and feelings of omnipotence

Some sufferers believe they are great religious leaders or other famous historical figures. Others believe they are responsible for everything that goes wrong in the world. Tina's first schizophrenic breakdown, at 16 years of age, coincided with the start of the Falklands War. She was convinced that she was to blame for the war and was responsible for all the suffering and deaths that followed.

Ideas of reference

Sufferers frequently become convinced that everything that happens refers to them. They switch on the television and find that what is being said refers to them or they turn on the radio to find that the music they are

21

listening to is interrupted by a news bulletin that mentions them by name. Careful avoidance of, or agitation about, the radio or television in someone you previously called 'square eyes' might be worth investigating if they are also turning into a stranger.

Similarly, sufferers may walk into a shop and recognise that 'double talk', as they call it, is going on, with everyone discussing them 'in code'. Even the rubbing of a nose or tapping of a foot can be interpreted as a sign that a message about them is being relayed to the rest of the people in the room. So real is this experience that I have seen a young man reduced to tears before rushing out again.

Delusions of poverty

More rarely, a sufferer may become convinced that the spending of any money, however little, will result in utter poverty. Such ideas led Mabel, an affluent widow, to starve herself and nearly perish from hypothermia because she believed she would end up 'in a debtor's prison in Paris' if she bought food or switched on the heating.

Sex-based delusions

These occur frequently and can be quite bizarre. One woman patient used to periodically announce that she was expecting a baby and that her pregnancy would last for several years.

Similarly, some sufferers become confused about sexual boundaries, so a son will perhaps make inappropriate advances to his mother who may be the only woman he sees anything of because he never leaves the house.

Confusion over one's sexual identity is also common. Bernard was tormented by the idea that he had suddenly become homosexual (something that was particularly painful for this man and which turned out to have no foundation whatever) and then insisted every passer-by could see he was now homosexual by looking at his face. Very soon he was refusing to leave the ward because of this.

Race-based delusions

A few sufferers experience what might be considered to be racist feelings, which are entirely out of character for them. They can be devastated by feelings of acute embarrassment and awareness that make it impossible for them to relate to anyone of a different race or colour. This was a feature of Marie's breakdown, despite the fact that one of her best friends from their schooldays is black and, when well again, she dated an Asian boy for some considerable time.

Religion-based delusions

A preoccupation with religious ideas is another frequent feature of psychosis, which many sufferers do anyway come to see as being an essentially spiritual experience.

Sadly, when this is associated with delusional ideas, this is more often a harrowing influence than a positive one, with some individuals feeling they have been singled out for punishment. Jean, a mild-mannered, middle-aged mother and housewife, had a visual hallucination featuring flashing lights, which neatly led into a delusion that she had been singled out for a 'visitation' because she had had two wartime affairs before her marriage. This, in turn, led to anguished and distorted feelings of guilt, shame and hopelessness.

Similarly, I have known several younger male sufferers who have searched the Bible for examples of mercy and forgiveness because they were convinced that they had been shown that they had been singled out for a future of hell and damnation.

Delusions of dying or wasting away

A small group of sufferers display hypochondriacal ideas, convinced that they are dying from an obscure physical condition, and some believe that parts of their body are melting and wasting away. So real are these ideas, that the first signs of mental illness in such sufferers may be frequent visits to their GP with a series of ailments that come to nothing. Sadly, doctors may not recognise what is behind these visits because their patients do not mention psychological or emotional problems, which is only natural as, of course, they do not believe they are mentally ill.

And so we come to what I call the core delusion of a schizophrenic illness – the 'I am not mentally ill' syndrome, which occurs at the point that the psychosis takes over. We will return to this topic when we look at what happens in a crisis in Chapters 9 and 10.

3 Problems with attention span and thought structure

Another type of symptom with this illness is the conviction that one's attention span and thoughts have taken on a life of their own. This may be experienced in several ways.

A 'captured' attention span

Some individuals have a startling type of experience, feeling as if their attention span is being controlled by an outside force. They may be reading or walking along the street or talking with someone when their attention is caught, and held, by some perhaps quite insignificant object. It might be anything – a single word on a page or an empty sweet packet on the pavement or a ring on a friend's hand – that holds the individual's attention and they are transfixed, unable to turn away. This leads – quite predictably – to a conviction that this particular object has some special meaning that they are meant to decipher.

Sufferers affected in this way find that all sorts of things take on this special meaning or *heightened* significance as it is called. Amazing and inspirational theories tend to evolve from such convictions, leading to even more confusion between themselves and those around them.

A blank mind

Many sufferers report that their mind goes completely blank, leaving them 'empty' and confused as all the thoughts in their head have been taken from them. Some are convinced that this has indeed happened and that their thoughts are being broadcast for all to hear – a truly awesome thought!

Intrusive thoughts

Conversely, perhaps one of the most distressing symptoms of this type of illness are the uninvited thoughts that 'someone is putting in my mind' which go round and round incessantly in the individual's head. Keith, a natural-born teacher who loves children, was so tormented at one time by persistent thoughts that he was about to assault a child that, at one point, he refused to leave his home for weeks in case this was true. Equally, Dave, who adores animals and treats them with loving care, was continuously plagued by ideas that he should torture his pets. He found he could deal with this to an extent by talking about these thoughts whenever they came back to plague him.

These persistent and unwanted thoughts can cause considerable anguish precisely because they seem to be associated with the very things that are particularly abhorrent to that individual. It is as if those who suffer with this symptom – often really gentle people in my experience – have focused in on the worst thing they could ever do and are then tormented with the idea that they will actually act in this way.

Perhaps this last point is particularly significant. The more one looks at the various psychotic experiences in any one acute schizophrenic illness, the more they may seem to reflect the worst fears of that particular sufferer.

Chronic schizophrenia

We refer to the cluster of features which represent the chronic form of this illness as 'negative' symptoms because they take something away from the individual's experience. All of the following will probably be experienced on a more or less permanent basis.

Apathy

This is probably the core feature of this illness – an apathy that robs the individual of any get up and go. Self-motivation of any kind is usually absent or very short-lived. There is often little inclination to do much more than sit and stare into space or lie in bed all day, and this, in turn, can escalate a withdrawal from others.

Lethargy

This can be crippling in its effect, with the individual experiencing profound mental and physical exhaustion. You might have felt something similar just after a severe bout of flu. It is important to bear in mind how this feels as the sufferer may appear to be able-bodied and strong while being quite unable to work.

Poverty of speech

A prominent feature of this type of illness, it refers to an individual's inability to make conversation and, in particular, to engage in the small talk that is so much a part of our everyday life. Most sufferers can still take part in the sort of conversation that works on a question and answer basis, so long as they are not expected to ask the questions themselves and they do not perceive the questioner to be intruding on them in any way.

Flatness

Brian says he has only distant memories of what it feels like to experience the ups and downs of everyday life, to feel excitement and pain, to look forward to something, to become immersed in a book or television programme or to enjoy a favourite food. None of these things touch him now, and he misses them: 'life is grey', he says, 'it's like being part of a barren desert'.

Blunting of emotion

This is the feature of the chronic illness that most upsets those closest to sufferers. It seems that the individual has lost any feeling or concern for others. Indeed, received wisdom tends to confirm that sufferers are self-absorbed to the point of indifference about what goes on around them. In the course of my work, though, I have had heartening evidence to the contrary and I shall return to this sensitive topic in Chapter 12.

An overlap of symptoms

We have just looked at the typical picture of the chronic form of schizophrenia. Importantly, flatness and blunting of emotions are likely to be specific to the *chronic* illness, whereas other 'negative' symptoms may be experienced for a while after an acute breakdown. Similarly, there are a few other symptoms and experiences that overlap both conditions, as follows:

Lack of eye contact

It is not clear why this is a frequent feature in a schizophrenic illness, but it is. Medical notes often start with the comment 'better eye contact today', and this is certainly an outward sign of less inner torment. Mick was told, by an otherwise caring and friendly nurse on the first occasion they met, 'Look at me, please, when I'm talking to you!', Mick could neither comply nor explain, but, fortunately, they were able to laugh about this much later.

Upturning of the 24-hour clock

It is quite common for sufferers to feel exhausted and sleep most of the day and to 'come to life' late at night. This can cause considerable distress to sufferers and be the greatest barrier to resuming a normal life. I well remember Susan begging me to call for her one morning so that she would not miss a group outing. I managed to get her up and out in time to meet the rest of the group, only to discover her fast asleep on her feet in a crowded and bustling store an hour later.

Changed eating patterns

Many sufferers develop a craving for stodgy junk food and have no interest in more nutritional foods. For some, this craving takes the form of ravaging for available food as if they were a starving animal – good manners and sharing seem to be a thing of the past! Sandra was very embarrassed by her need to devour foods in this way. An athletic young woman eating a sensible diet before her illness, she found herself cooking trays of buns to eat between meals – she couldn't stop herself eating a dozen cakes at a time. Thankfully her appetite returned to normal as her illness waned.

A further overlap of symptoms

This abnormal craving for certain foods can be seen in MD, too, and may well be a feature of psychosis generally rather than of any one illness in particular. Similarly, a changed sleeping pattern is commonly found in mania and depression as well as in both types of schizophrenia.

As we have seen, depression and chronic schizophrenia are both characterised by a slowing down of the personality, a lack of energy and drive and a lack of staying power. With both illnesses, there is a pronounced tendency to withdrawal, too. Also, it is common to find feelings of anxiety, guilt and self-loathing – all features of a depressive illness – in schizophrenia sufferers, particularly during an acute episode. Although schizophrenia is not a mood disorder like MD, it is very common, nevertheless, for schizophrenia sufferers to be depressed. One study has revealed that as many as 70 per cent of sufferers may be treated for clinical depression during the two years following an acute episode.

Furthermore, although they have been listed here under the heading of acute schizophrenia, hallucinations and delusions can feature in severe depression and mania, too, because they are a feature of psychosis, a feature of losing touch with reality. In particular, delusions of grandeur and omnipotence, religion-based delusions and paranoid ideas are common in mania. Similarly, although they have been listed here under the heading of mania, flight of ideas and pressure of speech may also feature in an acute schizophrenic episode.

Summing up

It may be clear by now that schizophrenia and MD have at least as many features in common as they do differences between them. The good news, as we shall see, is that the psychotic symptoms of these illnesses are eminently treatable, as are the excessive mood swings that used to devastate the lives of many MD sufferers.

3

About medical treatment

It is probably fair to say that few of us *like* taking medication. We don't like to feel we need to take drugs to keep well and we don't like taking them once we feel well. Perhaps most of all, we don't like the hassle of the unwanted side-effects associated with medication or any restrictions that taking them may place on our lives.

An old colleague of mine used to impress on groups of student nurses how it feels to have to take medication regularly and she would start by challenging them to confirm that they had never given up on completing a course of antibiotics because their symptoms had gone. She found that few could do this, reflecting a common resistance to persevering with drugs, even when there are known risks associated with discontinuing them.

This is a salutary reminder that no one should underrate the frustration felt by those who need to take medication continuously to prevent a recurrence of a serious mental illness, particularly for those who have to put up with unwanted side-effects as well.

A special case

Unfortunately, this reluctance to persevere with taking medication is further aggravated by two factors specific to this type of illness. First, at the point of becoming psychotic, sufferers don't believe that they actually have an illness and many have lingering doubts about this when they are well again, too!

Second, as we noted briefly in Chapter 1, a significant minority of those who work with or write and campaign about psychosis are also ambivalent about it being an illness. Some of them insist that the prescribed medication is nothing more than a 'chemical strait-jacket', a way of sedating and keeping the patient quiet. In the circumstances, this is not only unhelpful, it is also untrue, as those sufferers who are well enough to live an active and normal lifestyle, with the help of their medication, can testify!

Another reason given for not prescribing medication is that the drugs bring with them unwanted side-effects and risks. This, of course, is true of all drugs, and those used in psychiatry are no worse in this respect than those used in general medicine. Warts and all, the modern drugs have changed the face of serious mental illness and perhaps it would be fair to acknowledge that they have, mercifully, *removed* the need for strait-jackets rather than represent a new form of restraint as cynics suggest.

One way or another, there is a lot to discourage sufferers from persevering with their medication, and a significant minority choose not to, often with dire results. Many more learn to live with having to take medication only as a result of hard experience and one relapse too many. A new and encouraging trend in the United States, which is now being promoted in the UK, too, by members of the Manic Depression Fellowship, is for sufferers to have more responsibility for their own health rather than being expected to passively comply with a treatment programme prepared for them by others. This self-management approach can be very relevant to this discussion about taking medication and we'll come back to it in the next chapter.

Let's now take a look at the drugs which started the revolution that led to the advent of community care.

Neuroleptic drugs

These drugs sometimes used to be known as major tranquillisers, but this name is rarely used now because it leads to confusion with the minor tranquillisers, which are notoriously addictive as well as being primarily sedative in effect. The neuroleptic drugs are neither addictive nor primarily sedative in effect, but have a specific effect on the brain chemistry involved in the sorts of symptoms typical of a psychotic breakdown. They are the drugs of choice for the treatment of the typical bizarre symptoms of an acute schizophrenic episode and may also be used as a temporary measure in manic or depressive psychosis.

Before the discovery in the early 1950s that this group of drugs had such a specific effect on psychotic symptoms, the majority of sufferers not only languished in the old mental hospitals indefinitely, but they also had little relief from their tormenting symptoms. Nurses and doctors working in the NHS at the time have vivid memories of what it was like for those who suffered from a serious mental illness before modern drugs became available for use on the old hospital wards. Some of the patients who had previously been too dangerous or withdrawn to be approached in any way were transformed when prescribed this medication. They gradually began to reach out to others and start talking about the past, about children they had perhaps never mentioned nor seen for many years, about their lives before they became ill. Some were even able to successfully pick up the threads of these former lives once more.

Once the excitement and euphoria of watching these daily miracles had died down, it became more clear that the drugs did not cure a schizophrenic illness, but, if they were taken regularly, provided enough relief from psychotic symptoms in some patients for them to make a gradual recovery and become well enough to leave hospital.

A continuing treatment – not a cure

Those patients who 'bounced back' again after taking these drugs often turned out to be the ones who did not bother to persevere with the medication outside of hospital or kept forgetting to take them. This served to emphasise that the drugs had a vital role to play beyond that of breaking through and controlling psychosis. Indeed, research carried out throughout the years since this medication was first used has continued to confirm that for those who come off it, there is an 80 per cent risk of relapse during the following couple of years.

Tablets or injections?

Before very long, drug companies started to provide the medication in an oil base, to be given as 'depot' injections, as well as in the existing tablet form. These are usually given at fortnightly, three-weekly or four-weekly intervals and can provide a more stable supply of medication than is possible with tablets. They can also provide extra protection for the sufferer by removing the need to remember to take tablets each day.

Provided that injections are given as part of a personal and caring monitoring service, ensuring that at least *one* professional is regularly involved with the individual and thus made aware of any problems that may arise, then having the medication prescribed as an injection can be a very positive part of a treatment programme. I don't believe it's a coincidence that most of the really well sufferers I have known have been prescribed injections and have chosen to stay with these indefinitely. However, such a decision has usually depended on such factors as whether or not the individual had good or adverse experiences with starting medication at the time of a first breakdown and on the supervising doctor's own attitude to injections, rather than on any carefully thought out plan of action, and this is another matter that might come more into focus if the principles of self-management on the part of patients become a viable option for those having to cope with a serious mental illness.

What does the medication do?

There are four groups of these drugs. All fulfil much the same function, but have slightly different properties that suit one person better than another, resulting in some trial and error in establishing which drug is right for a particular individual.

A main function of these drugs seems to be that of restricting an excess of dopamine (a neurotransmitter or 'nerve messenger') in the brain cells of individuals experiencing the positive symptoms so typical of acute schizophrenia. There's little doubt that this surplus dopamine produces these symptoms, but we don't know why it should be there in the first place. Meanwhile, although sometimes it is a trial and error process to initially find the right drug, in the majority of cases, the medication effectively calms the over-roused patient within a day or two and begins to have a significant effect on the worst symptoms of a psychotic breakdown about two weeks later.

Unwanted side-effects

Unfortunately, the drugs do not just target the brain cells and this means that they can also unnecessarily restrict the amount of dopamine available to other cells in the body. This causes some sufferers to experience any of a cluster of symptoms reminiscent of Parkinson's disease, an illness characterised by a shortage of dopamine. These pronounced tremors and various other Parkinson's-type symptoms can cause profound distress for those affected by them if they are not controlled. However, they do respond to the drugs prescribed for Parkinson's disease and many sufferers who have to take these initially find they are able to come off this antidote medication quite soon.

A more serious matter

Whereas these and most other side-effects of this type of medication are of a temporary nature, there has been much publicity about the risks of a more serious side-effect – a condition called tardive dyskinesia. This condition manifests itself in involuntary movements of the facial muscles, particularly of the tongue and mouth, and it is difficult to treat successfully.

Although it existed before the use of these drugs and can also be seen in elderly individuals who have never been treated with them, it is claimed that tardive dyskinesia is very much associated with neuroleptic drug treatment, particularly with long-term treatment and in the elderly. It is not at all clear just what this association may be, although the routine, ongoing use of the antidote medication we discussed above is now believed to be implicated and discouraged for this reason and the

31

'stopping and starting' of neuroleptic drugs may also increase the risk. However, estimates of the extent of the incidence of tardive dyskinesia vary so much as to make them meaningless and it may be worth mentioning that this distressing condition is not something that I or several of my colleagues who have been working in this area for a long time have seen at all often in the course of our work. Meanwhile, however, the search continues for medication that precludes this worrying risk, as well as lessening other side-effects.

A fine balance

The role of medication in helping sufferers avoid unnecessary relapses is all a question of finding that fine balance between limiting the damage of a potentially damaging psychosis and minimising any discomforts or risks arising from the medication that can achieve this. How important it is to find this balance becomes more clear when we realise that a relapse usually calls for the prescription of relatively enormous amounts of the same medication that can be taken in small, regular doses to minimise the risk of relapse.

Over recent years, the search for drugs that will have fewer Parkinson's-type side-effects and also help those whose symptoms are resistant to the traditional drugs, has resulted in several atypical antipsychotic drugs being introduced. Two of these are gaining a reputation for helping this group of patients and for being the first to have some effect on the negative symptoms of schizophrenia. This may be an important breakthrough as the traditional drugs have done little to combat the misery of this type of illness, although a lot of chronic sufferers need to take them to avoid relapses into an acute episode.

At the time of writing, a further batch of atypical drugs are due to be released in the near future, but it must be said that whereas newer drugs are combating some of the Parkinson's type side-effects of the older ones and bringing definite benefits for some individuals whose illness has previous been resistant to treatment, they also tend to produce side-effects and risks of their own.

Let's now take a look at the medication used to control the excessive swings of mood that used to cause so much devastation in the lives of many MD sufferers.

Lithium

Lithium is the first choice medication for MD. It is a natural substance, a salt found in minerals derived from food and water in our diet. The main role of lithium in the treatment of this illness is as preventive medication.

It stabilises mood swings by influencing the action of neurotransmitters in the brain.

Importantly, lithium is unlikely to have any positive effect for at least two weeks after it is first taken and it may take several months before its full preventive role is evident. However, patience may well be rewarded as an estimated 60 per cent of those who try lithium do well on it, particularly those who otherwise have excessive mood swings or frequent manic episodes.

Regular blood tests are essential so that blood levels of the drug can be monitored, as there is a fine line between providing enough lithium for it to be effective and ensuring that amounts of the drug in the blood don't reach toxic levels. It is important, therefore, that sufferers and those closest to them are aware of the need for caution (more information can be obtained on this and the potential side-effects of taking lithium and other drugs used in MD from the Manic Depression Fellowship – their address is given in the Useful addresses section at end of this book).

Other stabilizing drugs

Carbamezepine, also used in the treatment of epilepsy, may be used as an alternative to lithium or in conjunction with it. It is also thought to influence neurotransmitter activity, acting as a mood stabiliser and antimanic agent. Again, around 60 per cent of individuals prescribed this drug do well on it.

Sodium valproate is a third drug that may be successfully prescribed where sufferers don't respond to or cannot tolerate lithium or carbamazepine.

All of these drugs are used to control excessive mood swings, so their main function is to prevent relapse into a manic or depressive illness. This means that most sufferers need to take them indefinitely. Very occasionally, they will also be prescribed a neuroleptic drug as an alternative or extra preventive measure, but, more often, this type of medication will be used when patients are psychotic and at immediate risk because of this.

Antidepressant drugs

When they are depressed, MD sufferers are likely to be prescribed antidepressant drugs to be taken on their own or in conjunction with lithium or carbamazepine. There are at least three groups of antidepressants and which of these drugs is chosen will depend on the individual nature of each depression. For example, some can be particularly helpful where lack of appetite and sleep are the main problems, while others are better where anxiety and agitation are predominant. Some are more sedative in their effect than others and one group of drugs, usually prescribed for an atypical depression, can create problems because of how they interact with certain foods and other drugs.

No antidepressants take effect immediately and some can take up to four weeks, sometimes more, to start to have an influence on a depressive illness. Although this can seem like forever at the time, once the right drug and right dosage have been found, the wait will later fade into insignificance.

It might be worth noting here that there is a general tendency to come off the medication too soon, so it may be wise to persevere for some time after the depression starts to wane, unless, of course, there are signs of the mood lifting too much and so perhaps pre-empting a manic attack.

Another type of medical treatment

Where a depression becomes entrenched and proves to be resistant to all the various types of available medication, then there is another treatment doctors may wish to consider using – electoconvulsive therapy (ECT). Much less commonly, it may also have a place in severe mania as well.

Although this has dwindled recently, ECT has had a bad press over the past ten years and has been the subject of considerable controversy. Much of this has been concerned with undoubted abuses in the past and by claims from some individuals that the treatment has a permanent effect on the memory, as well as by cynicism over the use of such an intrusive treatment – one that induces the patient to have a fit – when we have no idea how and why it works.

However, the debate has calmed down now and some psychiatrists and other mental health professionals as well as some patients have no doubt whatever that the skilled use of ECT can be effective and particularly so where all else fails. It is not so uncommon for patients who have discovered this for themselves to actually request this treatment because it has helped them in the past. However, many more patients become very concerned about the possibility of being given ECT and much of their fear may be associated with all the adverse publicity it has been given.

It is really very important that patients, and anyone else who is interested, should have an opportunity to find out more about this treatment, and there is a useful special report entitled *ECT: Pros, Cons and Consequences* published by MIND (available from MIND and from the Manic Depression Fellowship – see the Useful addresses section at the back of the book for the address of the latter). Meanwhile, the following comment on ECT treatment taken from the Fellowship's own paper entitled *Manic Depressive Disorder* may help quell some fears:

> . . . the patient is given a muscle relaxant and a short-lasting general anaesthetic. A strictly controlled electrical current is passed across the brain from electrodes placed against the head. Frequently, there is a loss of memory for the period of treatment but there is no evidence for long-term effects on memory. Generally a deep-seated mood is successfully shifted.

Summing up

There can be no doubt that the treatment of serious mental illness is the subject of considerable controversy, both among sufferers and those involved in a continuing debate about whether or not psychosis is a treatable 'entity' or a truly remarkable consequence of an imperfect world. However, every argument sinks into insignificance in the face of a raging and untreated psychosis and our inability to do anything at all to help those caught up in it unless they are given the appropriate medication. Similarly, there is little chance of sufferers being able to successfully get on with the rest of their lives unless they can keep the psychosis at bay and, once again, this can only be achieved in many, if not most, cases by continuing to take medication. It is only at this point that all sorts of things become possible. Let's now take a look at some of them.

4

What else helps?

In the last chapter, we looked at the vital role medication has to play in controlling a serious mental illness. This achieved, sufferers are only likely to fulfil their potential and have a rewarding lifestyle if information about the illness is made available so that they can understand their own vulnerability and take responsibility for keeping well and avoiding relapse.

This being the case, it is a great pity that first-time sufferers are frequently told very little about what has happened to them by professionals and, even more importantly, about what they can do to protect themselves from relapse. This unsatisfactory state of affairs has led, inevitably, to the growth of a strong self-help movement, with specialist organisations providing information, advice and access to up-to-date research. More recently, one of these – the Manic Depression Fellowship – has responded to its members' growing interest in self-management and has focused on the potential advantages of sufferers developing more expertise and knowledge about their condition and having a greater say in their treatment.

Self-management

In theory, self-management can mean that one sufferer might choose to comply completely with a doctor's recommendations while another might choose to decline to take medication, but might seek professional help with this. In practice, however, self-management is *not* anti-medication and most sufferers will settle for something between these two extremes as many individuals find they need medication if they are to have choices in other aspects of their lives.

Over the past year or so, there has been a continuing discussion about different aspects of self-management in the Manic Depression Fellowship's journal, *Pendulum*, and it is clear that the various aspects of taking medication figure highly in members' concerns. One initiative that has resulted from this discussion is the proposal to design a brief agreement to be signed by patient and doctor which states that when the individual is feeling vulnerably 'high' or 'low', he or she may take a certain additional or reduced amount of an appropriate medication as a protective measure.

Such an agreement provides the necessary permission to take this precautionary measure without the sort of fuss and bother that can put sufferers off seeking help. Also, it serves to remind the individual of the safe dosage that has been previously agreed when there is a need to feel secure about what dose to take. This can then be taken when access to a professional may not be possible, for example late at night or at weekends.

A precedent

I have seen something similar to this work very well for a few privileged and potentially well schizophrenia sufferers – mainly on regular, low-dose injections – whose GPs have been happy to give them control over their health on a day-to-day basis by allowing them to have a small quantity of extra medication to use if they find they are experiencing symptoms and feeling vulnerable. Such an arrangement acknowledges a fact that is well-known but much neglected, which is that, at times, sufferers need more medication than at others, for whatever reason. This simple fact can put individuals with a serious mental illness at greater risk than any other feature of the illness because the system simply does not allow for it!

Having access to a temporarily increased dose immediately it is needed can forestall a potential relapse and allows sufferers to take responsibility for their own health, rather than having to rush around trying to obtain a prescription for extra medication at a time when this may not be possible and when they are speedily losing confidence in themselves and trust in others.

A vital critical period

Such a readily available precautionary measure can make the difference between staying well or suffering repeated long and protracted relapses, because there is a short critical time during which the sufferer recognises that something is going wrong and will accept help. Once the psychosis sets in, it is too late.

Working in partnership

In the United States, the move towards self-management by MD sufferers has led to their formulating written and signed statements that detail the conditions under which they will be prepared to accept (and would expect for their own protection) enforced hospitalization and treatment if they become too ill to realise they need help. Such statements allow for the detailing of treatments that have helped the individual in the past and vetoing of those they find unacceptable. They also allow for the naming of trusted individuals to act as a group and make this important decision on the sufferer's behalf – a kind of living will or advance directive (see Mary Ellen Copeland's books, listed in the Further reading section at the back of this book). This would equally meet the needs of many schizophrenia sufferers I know who dread that everything they have strived for might be devastated by one further breakdown. The full importance of being able to take this sort of action becomes clear later, in Chapters 9 and 10.

Accessing information

Perhaps the first priority of a self-management approach has to be obtaining information. If you are at this stage, then a good place to start might be to ask any professionals involved in your care to answer basic questions about your diagnosis and any proposed or existing treatment. You might find a pharmacist will be helpful in answering questions about your medication and possible risks associated with taking or not taking it. You might also like to talk to other sufferers about their experiences. If you don't know any, then perhaps professionals can help you contact others like yourself. If not, then specialist organisations, such as the Manic Depression Fellowship and the National Schizophrenia Fellowship (for their addresses, see the Useful addresses section at the back of the book), should certainly be able to point you in the right direction and they can also provide advice and literature on your illness, about its treatment and about various other aspects of coping generally.

Know your illness

Even as you digest all the information you can obtain from others who have been there, mental health workers and any available up-to-date literature, you will almost certainly be building up knowledge about your own illness and how best you can deal with it. For example, if you are an MD sufferer, what makes you high or low? Is it better for you to avoid too much excitement, even seemingly enjoyable but heated debate with friends? Do you find that being alone too much, or, perhaps, drinking more than a moderate amount of alcohol makes your mood plummet? Are you learning what the signs are that things are going wrong with you? Can you help yourself at such times by cancelling appointments, by not answering the phone or by sitting listening to music you find comforting?

If you are a schizophrenia sufferer, do you find that certain situations tend to make you feel self-conscious and even slightly paranoid? Do you find changes of any kind difficult and unsettling? Are you one of those who find being alone much of the time starts your mind racing and creates feelings of agitation?

If you can, get to know your illness and what helps you and, conversely, how certain things you do tend to make you more vulnerable. Look for ways to help yourself keep unwanted symptoms at bay and get to know the signs that should be a warning that things may be going wrong.

A social network

If you find yourself relatively isolated in your efforts to cope with what has happened to you, perhaps through having no family or close friends at hand, then it becomes even more important to have access to fellow sufferers and also to seek the ongoing support of a small group of well-trusted individuals (these could be relatives or friends or mental health workers or even a mix of all of these) who know how you are when you are really well and who also understand what happens to you when you are ill and how this affects you. This is something MD sufferers are starting to do as part of a self-management programme and there are obvious benefits to be had by having a 'support group' such as this whose members can keep a friendly eye on you by watching out for any signs of deterioration in your health and backing you in seeking immediate help for this. Ideally, they can also ensure that someone can be available at times of stress to meet with you or to talk and listen on the telephone and offer reassurance when this is needed. A fellow sufferer may well make a welcome and especially valued member of such a group, particularly if he or she has known you when you've been completely well – that is, the real you!

Dealing with the present

If the most important aspect of self-management means taking responsibility for oneself and for staying as well as is possible, it might be a good starting point to avoid wasting energy on looking for someone or something to blame for what has happened. Where there is a paranoid element in a serious mental illness, this sort of scapegoating can happen anyway and can be fanned by a tendency among some professionals to encourage sufferers to look for a scapegoat for their troubles. Families, and one's past (which cannot anyway be changed) have tended to be favourite scapegoats and this can be very sad as it can lead to exhausting and frustrating negative feelings and to alienating some of those who probably have the most reason to care about protecting the sufferer's interests. Too many families have broken up this way. Attempting to find reasons for having a psychotic illness is to ignore the indiscriminate way it attacks so many members of every society.

It is wiser to save one's energy and humour for making sure that the future is as positive as possible and saving the inevitable feelings of resentment – and, perhaps, a healthy need to rant and rave – for the illness itself.

A sensible lifestyle

After becoming stabilised on the right treatment and seeking all the available information on what has happened to you, the next priority will probably be to attempt to adopt a sensible lifestyle, one that is both stimulating and rewarding. This will be relatively simple if you are living with your family or in a hostel or other situation where there is a good chance that someone else may provide a bed, warmth and comfort, regular meals and a sensible diet, regardless of what finances you may have available.

If you are living on your own, however, then this can all be a very different ball game, as you will know if you are in this situation! If this is the case, then it can be helpful to focus on trying to adopt some sort of routine that can provide a feeling of structure and shape to your day. As you may know only too well already, none of this is as simple as it may sound and it can take considerable self-discipline to organise a day-to-day routine, let alone carry this out. As with all things, success is most likely if you are patient and kind to yourself. More will be achieved by setting reasonable and attainable goals to be achieved one by one than reaching for the moon.

Factors that can be unhelpful

Meanwhile, and more urgently, there is a need to take note of factors that can be really bad news for so many individuals with a serious mental illness. Too much excitement and unwanted changes can be harmful, as can lack of sleep and inadequate nutrition. More importantly, abusing alcohol by drinking more than a moderate amount can make sufferers more vulnerable by adversely affecting mood and by interacting with their medication. In particular, taking street drugs such as LSD and cannabis can make the difference between schizophrenia sufferers having the potential to make a good recovery or becoming virtually untreatable.

Some sufferers turn to illegal drugs or alcohol for relief from unexplained symptoms during the frequently long delays before help and a diagnosis are obtained. Others are more likely to become dependent on them because they have the sort of addictive personality that is sometimes associated with a serious mental illness. Either way, it may be very difficult to give up such a habit once it has become established, but the best way to go about this, if it has, can be to adopt a lifestyle that can minimise the opportunities and temptation to maintain it.

Roy

Roy found it even more difficult to give up his old friends and acquaintances than to give up his drug habit. He missed them and his previous lifestyle so much that he went back to them again and again. Each time this happened, he resumed taking cannabis and each time he was plagued once more with his 'voices' and delusional ideas. Eventually, a mental health worker suggested that Roy take up some nightschool studies he had often spoken about and also persuaded him to offer to help in the kitchen at a local drop in centre for a few hours each week. Roy soon made one or two new contacts with similar interests to his own and eventually he succeeded in giving up cannabis and has made a good recovery. Several times since he has told other sufferers struggling with the same sort of problem that, after a few months of giving up taking cannabis, he had found that his medication was at last giving him real relief from his schizophrenic symptoms. Roy has no doubt at all that the worst years of his illness were associated with his drug habit.

On a less serious note, caffeine seems to be the drug of choice for many sufferers and this can serve to 'wind-up' one's mood as well as one's blood pressure. This is where a structured routine can help as being busy can take one's mind off having yet another cup of tea or coffee (and another cigarette, where the person smokes).

It does take a lot of organising to find ways to protect oneself from undesirable excesses, but it may be very worth while in the long run.

What else helps?

Well, you may be asking at this stage, so much for all the effort that the *sufferer* has to make, but, apart from medical treatment, what can *others* offer to compliment this self-management?

Pros and cons of 'talking therapies'

As a general rule, most professionals involved in this sort of work are aware that any probing or analytic approach can be intrusive and threatening for someone with a serious mental illness. However, some sufferers find supportive psychotherapy helpful, when this focuses on finding ways to cope on a day-to-day basis with having a serious mental illness and to come to terms with this and with the way society reacts to it.

Cognitive therapy

This is one of the newer talking therapies and has a unique place among them because instead of focusing on what has happened to the client in the past, it concentrates on the here and now and important matters such as the individual's self-esteem.

This method of working has now been adapted by some clinical psychologists for use with people with schizophrenia and treatment trials have shown that it can be of use in helping sufferers to cope better with any lingering voices and delusional beliefs. It can also focus on the feelings of worthlessness so common in this illness.

Although results have so far have been positive, cognitive therapy is not intended to be a treatment for the illness but, rather, a way of relieving distress associated with it. It is very important to check that a therapist has a proper understanding of schizophrenic illness and has appropriate training – and that there is ongoing supervision – for this work. It may be a very good idea to contact the National Schizophrenia Fellowship Advice Line (see the Useful addresses section at the back of the book for the number) and seek further information and advice about cognitive therapy if you are interested.

Please note that it seems that the jury is still out on using cognitive therapy for MD sufferers. However, there are moves to find ways to adapt this approach to MD, with sufferers being asked to contribute to this work (now that does sound like a true partnership!) The Manic Depression Fellowship can provide more information on this (for their address, see the Useful addresses section at the back of the book).

Group work

In much the same way as happened with many talking therapies, the sort of group work commonly used in the mental health services has proved largely unsuitable for individuals with a serious mental illness. These groups tend, by their very nature, to be too unstructured and unsettling for MD and schizophrenia sufferers, and the more extreme encounter-type groups can be positively dangerous for them.

After years of watching my schizophrenic clients going to extraordinary lengths to avoid mandatory groups in hospital and then markedly avoiding groups offered outside of hospital, I spent some time trying to find out why both they and group therapists agreed that schizophrenia and groups just did not mix. As a result of this, I was eventually privileged to find myself in a position to pioneer groups for schizophrenia sufferers that they actually *asked* to join and which some of them attended for up to several years at a time, even if it meant finding, and paying, their own way to whatever venue we were able to find for them.

Very briefly, these small groups are made up of around six to eight members, all with a schizophrenic or similar illness. On the one hand, the groups run on self-help lines, with members talking about themselves and things that matter to them and sharing their experiences, with ways of coping and advice for each other. On the other, the groups are unique in that they also have a directive leader who provides a structured and safe environment with firm and mutually understood boundaries. All members thus feel secure and have their own space and time, with no one hogging the limelight or being left out, as so often happens in less structured groups.

I have described these groups in detail in my recent book, *Working with Schizophrenia* (see the Further reading section at the end of the book for details) and, having successfully trained volunteers to work in this way, I suspect that this sort of group could be run by well-recovered sufferers and by carers, as well as by others showing an appropriate aptitude, if some training and ongoing supervision could be made available.

Reality testing

One other therapy that I pioneered in my work with schizophrenia sufferers, and which is also described in some detail in *Working with Schizophrenia*, has been described by a client, who was my first 'guinea pig', as the most important part of her eventual and excellent recovery.

I mentioned in Chapter 2 how Pat was plagued by a 'voice' in her head that mimicked her father's voice and kept threatening to kill her. Perhaps understandably, although she then understood that she had been hallucinating at the time, she continued to have paranoid ideas about him for a long time afterwards. It soon became clear that, although she was seeming to recover very well, Pat was occasionally hearing both her parents' 'voices', criticising her late at night when she was very tired. Fortunately, she mentioned doubts in one of her more confident moments because she could not understand why, when she glanced up, neither seemed to be moving their lips!

With her agreement, it was arranged that she and her parents would make and sign a contract. She would find the courage to challenge them each time she heard these 'voices' and they, in turn, would always find the time to deal with her distress and to reassure her that they had not spoken. In the event, Pat only ever managed a sharp, embittered, '*What did you say*?', but it was enough; her parents knew what this meant. They would spend time immediately, talking through with her what had happened – the saying 'watch my lips' took on a new meaning in this context! Pat invariably went up to bed relaxed and relieved. Her parents, nevertheless, found it quite harassing to be reminded each time of the torment this illness could still cause their daughter, who seemed to be well so much of the time. Many a peaceful and happy evening was spoiled for them until they realised that Pat was gradually learning to distinguish for herself what was real and what was a trying symptom of a lingering illness. The intervals between these incidents began to lengthen and, after a year or so, they became very rare indeed.

Meanwhile, Pat had found she could use what she called this 'reality testing' to engage the help of one or two close and trusted friends in similar circumstnaces outside of the home. She was delighted to find that they saw this as a compliment and they were pleased to reassure her when she felt vulnerable. Pat and her family were delighted with this approach, as others have been since, and it may be that it can help you as well.

Alternative therapies

Some sufferers have found alternative therapies helpful and speak highly of various different types. We are really talking about therapies that may be complimentary to taking medication.

Meditation and yoga seem to be particularly helpful for some individuals, while I have found that others may benefit from a dietary approach, particularly those who crave sweet and stodgy foods and who put on weight with their medication (I have written about this in *Schizophrenia. A fresh approach*, the details of which are given in the Further reading section at the back of the book).

Sometimes getting to know about alternative therapies may help you to adopt a more healthy lifestyle, but, on the whole, I have the impression that sufferers with various different serious disabilities tend to benefit perhaps more on a temporary, rather than a permanent, basis. If you decide to explore an alternative therapy, do remember to check on the authenticity and training of individual therapists and do beware of spending money you can ill afford.

Taking exercise

This is something that some sufferers find very helpful. Moderate exercise, especially taken in the fresh air, can be exhilarating and stimulating. It will be particularly beneficial if you can also take up some activity you really enjoy, whether it is swimming, playing tennis, cycling or walking in the countryside.

Summing up

Perhaps the most encouraging thing about this discussion on things that can compliment medical treatment is that we seem to have focused on approaches that rely on you taking responsibility for what happens and on others being prepared to engage in partnership with you to achieve this. Perhaps this bodes well for the future of self-management.

5

Coming to terms with what has happened

In the first chapters of this book we have looked at what can happen in MD and schizophrenia and discussed ways of coping with the aftermath of a breakdown. Having focused initially on these immediate practical issues, perhaps it is time to consider more carefully some of the seemingly mammoth problems that can all too easily overwhelm a sufferer at an emotional level. Let's take a closer look at the inner turmoil that can make it so hard to cope with what has happened.

Why me?

Perhaps the most common reaction – and the one most of the rest of us can identify with – is the silent, anguished, question, 'Why me? Why did this have to happen to *me*?'

If you are struggling to recover from a breakdown, then this is the question you have probably asked yourself again and again. At times like this, you could be forgiven for believing that everyone around you sails through life relatively untouched and you could choke with the injustice of it all. If you think this, it is understandable. While few of us *do* actually get by without our own share of trials and tribulations, it is certainly true that most are blissfully unaware about the sort of anguish a serious mental illness can wreak on its victims. Knowing that this is so becomes just another frustration to bear for the sufferer.

It is important, as well as healthy, to acknowledge such feelings. It is better to openly acknowledge anger and frustration than to bottle these up and allow them to fester. Our survival instinct comes into play at the point where feelings of anger start to move us on towards more positive thoughts, such as 'I'll show them. I'm not going to let this beat me' and later, perhaps, 'I can and will overcome this setback'.

If you are at this stage of recovering from a breakdown, it will almost certainly be a good idea to make sure you can meet with others who have been there, too, if you haven't already managed to do so. Professionals may be able to help here, but, if not, then the Manic Depression Fellowship or the National Schizophrenia Fellowship should be able to put you in touch with a local self-help group (see the Useful addresses section at the back of the book for their addresses). One of the advantages of meeting with other sufferers is that experiences and successes can be shared.

It may help to be aware that many individuals who have struggled with a serious mental illness have moved on from this point and have overcome what they can now refer to as a 'setback', albeit one of seemingly mammoth proportions at the time. Some have even reached the stage where, rather than feeling that they have lost out, they can actually look back and see that they have gained something along the way.

One survivor told me recently, 'this probably sounds a bit mad, but I'm not sorry this happened to me. I've had all sorts of experiences and met all sorts of people that have enriched my life'. I have heard similar heartening comments from others who have trodden the same road as this young woman. Several know themselves to be stronger, as well as more sensitive to others' problems, than before their illness. Nevertheless, one thing is certain, every one of them went through dire periods of feelings of desperation and self-pity along the way towards this realisation. While we're on the subject, for 'self-pity', read 'self-cosseting' – an urgent and real need to love, protect and pamper yourself, pending a return of the energy and fighting spirit that is a necessary part of recovery.

Grieving

Perhaps the hardest part of having a serious mental illness is coming to terms with what you may have lost as a result of it. For a small group of damaged sufferers, this can amount to a seemingly permanent loss of ordinary feelings of wellbeing and good health and, perhaps most serious of all, a feeling of having lost oneself. Fortunately, for most individuals, the losses will be much less severe and for some they will turn out to be temporary. Nevertheless, most will suffer painful loss *because* of their illness and this will be an extra cross to bear *on top of* their illness.

It is important not to hide these feelings of loss but, rather, that they be shared with others so that those around you are able to recognise how much, and why, you are grieving. It might be worth while discussing this with your GP, hospital doctor or, perhaps, a community psychiatric nurse, explaining that you would like to have some help with trying to cope with these perhaps profound feelings of loss in the aftermath of a psychotic breakdown. Losses may include the ending of an important relationship, a loss of dignity, of a home, of an opportunity to complete college studies, of a job, of a hard-earned and cherished career or even of a lifestyle that now seems as if it might be gone forever. On a very practical note, an MD sufferer may even be mourning financial losses from manic spending sprees!

Importantly, some or all of these losses may be temporary or even turn out to have been apparent rather than real once things settle down again, but, for the time being at least, they can amount to a genuine bereavement. Looking for ways to come to terms with this bereavement can eventually lead to finding ways to a more positive way forward and you may well feel you need help with this.

Stigma

All sorts of factors can contribute to the sort of loss we have been discussing and the most significant of these will probably be the effects of the stigma and ignorance surrounding serious mental illness.

What does one do about society's hang-ups? Isn't it enough that you have to cope with a serious illness without having to come to terms with the ill-informed attitudes of others? Maureen, a sufferer who has been well now for some years, told me once that although no one was unkind to her when she was recovering from her two breakdowns in hospital, she felt inhuman because none of the ward staff ever talked with her about her experiences or mentioned her illness. Maureen herself has come to terms with having a diagnosis of schizophrenia and she talks about it freely, but she wishes that health professionals would not shrink away from the reality of serious mental illness. As we noted in Chapter 1, such an attitude was very much the case with cancer several decades ago and it was cancer sufferers themselves who eventually brought their very common condition out into the open. It was only when public idols such as Hollywood film stars were prepared to say 'I have had cancer' that the shame and stigma began to fade and doctors started to talk more openly on the subject. Spike Milligan's 'coming out' may have helped to make MD something that members of the public now recognise and mention more comfortably but, at the time of writing, there is an increasing tendency for the public to associate schizophrenia with the sort of violence featured in newspaper horror headlines. Perhaps one day soon other famous stars will feel able to come out and say they have had a serious mental illness, with 'Look, this is no great deal for me'. Let's hope so! Meanwhile, until this happens and until those who work with this type of illness take on the responsibility of demystifying the whole subject, it does seem that it's left to sufferers and those who love them to do what they can to spread the word.

Remember that stigma applies to things that people don't understand

and are frightened by. It can be heartening to find how favourably close friends can react to the idea of a serious mental illness when they have an opportunity to identify this with someone they know well. Giving them the *chance* to understand, if and when this is right for you, can be rewarding and a step in the right direction. When you feel able to talk about this to people you trust, you will also be imparting an important message: stigma or not, you are not ashamed of having a common condition that tends to be associated with talented and potentially high achievers! This kind of message can also do wonders for damaged self-esteem.

Feelings of isolation

This might all sound very cheering and simple if it weren't for the fact that having a serious mental illness can leave you feeling very much alone – isolated and alienated from everyone around you, feeling that you are the only one this has happened to. This feeling is as much about the inner turmoil and one's perception of what is happening as it is about the way others are behaving. With time, the outside world should seem a less harsh place. This said, it is also about the way people avoid mentioning loss or death – they are not sure what to say, how to act. Similarly, they find it difficult to acknowledge and talk openly about what has happened when someone has had 'some sort of mental problem'. We deal rather better with *physical* illness, but, even then, we tend to be lost for the words that might very well lighten the load for the patient. A quick glance round an ordinary hospital ward during visiting time will confirm this phenomenon! A glance round a ward in a psychiatric hospital will be even more illuminating.

These feelings of isolation may be escalated by lingering symptoms of the illness. For a very long time – maybe a year or even considerably more than this – the symptoms may return at unexpected times, causing confusion and undermining one's grip on reality. These have been described by one sufferer as 'memories of the illness waiting in the shadows' and these are potentially damaging until the sufferer recognises them for what they are. They can be damaging because they can threaten one's perspective on what is happening, possibly reawakening paranoid ideas that loved ones cannot be trusted. Most of all, such feelings can make one feel very much alone, even when surrounded by family and friends. If this is how it is for you and you can find the courage to talk about what is happening to those who matter most, then they can help you to test reality (you might like to read about reality testing again in Chapter 4) until you recognise any lingering symptoms for what they are. This can take a very long time, but can be a worthwhile exercise, providing an increasingly firm grip on reality.

As you may know from personal experience, the side-effects of medication can also be very trying for some individuals in the early days of recovery. Once again, it is important to talk about this with family and with professionals to ensure that you are not having to put up with avoidable effects. Having done this, it is also important to persevere with your medication if you can and not to confuse residual symptoms of your illness with side-effects of the drug.

The need for self-acceptance

As we noted in Chapter 2, the depressive side of MD and schizophrenia can lead to feelings of worthlessness and guilt. These can be so profound that some of the nicest people I know refer to themselves as having been *evil* when they were ill. However much feelings relating to stigma may hurt and wound, they fade into insignificance when compared with the potential of this type of illness to make sufferers loathe themselves. This may be a part of these feelings of worthlessness or, for some, as part of their memories of how they behaved during a manic episode.

It can help to fully appreciate what is happening here. First, part of the inner turmoil and confusion that can follow on from a psychotic episode can wreak havoc with one's self-esteem. Second, this turmoil may be escalated by fears of what *may* have happened at the time of breakdown. Third, any depressive component of the illness will be accompanied by distorted feelings of guilt. Fourth, lingering delusions, together with, perhaps, occasional condemning 'voices', can reinforce any such self-loathing. If this has been your experience, you will know that, mercifully, as good health returns, so these feelings tend to fade. You will also appreciate that it is not at all surprising that your self-confidence has taken a battering. On top of all this, you may well have found that it was then up to you to put yourself together again!

Standing back a little and reading this may have made you wonder what sort of superhuman is meant to be able to cope with all of this? Surely, someone who can come through all of this has something more going for them than many seemingly more fortunate individuals? Surely, someone who can come through this harrowing test of strength, and survive, is, in fact, remarkably *strong?* The answer to these questions, based on my own experience of knowing and working with hundreds of sufferers, is a resounding *yes!*

A special kind of person

If you've got this far, you are a very special kind of person and a survivor. If you've any doubts about this, stop now, take a pause. Put the book down and think about it.

Now give yourself a hug – you are a survivor and this may be the moment for you to start to realise this and congratulate yourself.

Don't waste this inner strength. Start now to channel some of this strength into a routine task of rediscovering, and recording, each day one good, positive, thing about yourself. Keep a list and start it now with the first entry – I am strong – then spare a thought for tomorrow's entry. It won't be easy – some days it may seem desperately difficult but it can help you to become more objective about yourself.

A need to accept what has happened to you

If you haven't already done so, spare a little time to take on board what has happened to you. Perhaps the core of the inner turmoil left by a breakdown is the desire to wipe it out of one's consciousness, to believe it never happened. Don't give way to this temptation. Whatever type of serious mental illness you have suffered, it will not go away by pretending it never happened and, more to the point, it is far more likely to find an opportunity to return if you try to deny it.

Let me explain. It should be clear, perhaps by glancing back at Chapters 3 and 4 of this book, why it is so important to acknowledge one's illness and the havoc it can wreak on your life. Without this acknowledgement, you are unlikely to take careful note of what helps you and what doesn't help and learn to recognise any warning signs of a threatened relapse.

Without exception, those sufferers I have known who have recovered well enough to live a really normal life have learned first to accept their vulnerability to a serious mental illness. This has taken great courage – and yet more of that strength we have been discussing – because of the stigma, fear and ignorance presently attached to serious mental illness. It has been achieved once they have accepted and grown to love themselves again. This works on the honest 'take me, take my illness' principle and is very refreshing, if not irresistible! As it is quite a common phenomenon for sufferers to deny their illness, though, it may be worth pausing for a moment to consider why this should be.

It might well reflect justified horror about the whole experience (but, if so, shouldn't one's survival instinct be directed at preventing any recurrence?) Denial might reflect a 'head in the sand' approach to any future risks, and this may explain why a considerable number of sufferers eventually settle for acceptance of their illness and taking precautions to stay well only after maybe several breakdowns. In some cases, continued denial may reflect distorted feelings of shame and outrage about what has happened or, more worryingly, it may reflect a very frail hold on reality.

Whatever the cause, a denial of one's continuing vulnerability can, and usually does, block the way forward to coming to terms with what has happened and, thus, getting on with one's life. This is a great pity because this is, after all, a common type of illness that should not become an overwhelming problem for most sufferers if they remember to watch their lifestyle and do what they can to protect themselves from further breakdown.

Rather differently, some MD sufferers find the highs of their illness both enjoyable and productive. Not only do they enjoy the euphoria, but they also enjoy the undeniable fact that this can be a source of remarkable creativity. I suspect that most of us can identify with a natural reluctance to forego this sort of experience by making a determined effort to control the illness. Nevertheless, if this applies to you, can you really afford the costs in terms of the potential damage to your health, your relationships and your lifestyle, not to mention the pain of the depressive episodes that almost certainly follow the 'highs'?

Relationships with the family

Over the past three decades, the word 'family' has taken something of a bashing. This was never more true than for the relatives of sufferers of a serious mental illness and, in particular, schizophrenia. During the 1960s, it became fashionable to blame families for the sufferer's illness and it has to be said that, although these ideas (based as they were on flawed research) have long since been discredited, they remain 'alive and well' in the minds of some professionals. This means that it is all too easy for ideas originating from a sufferer's paranoid illness to be nurtured and flourish instead of being aired and resolved. As paranoia invariably focuses on those who matter most to the individual, this can have tragic results. It can lead to families breaking down for the want of the right sort of information, help and support.

My experience has taught me that sufferers need families and that families want to stay together. Nevertheless, mistakes will be made. After all, neither sufferers nor carers had any preparation or training for coping with a serious mental illness before this happened to them. Nor did either volunteer for such an experience!

We will be looking more closely at ways in which the family can be helped to understand just what does happen in this type of illness, but, meanwhile, there are one or two points that can be very important for individual sufferers to bear in mind because they are very much concerned with survival.

There can be no doubt that a psychotic illness can be an almost overwhelming experience, even when you have the wholehearted support of others who matter to you. Later, once relatively well again, close family members can be a vital resource in helping you protect yourself from further breakdown. Lastly, society offers very few viable alternatives to living with the family (or with the family's support, as the case may be). All in all, it may be very worth while persevering with family relationships, particularly for those sufferers who found them rewarding before their illness may have started to sour things.

The problem is an illness

Really, it may all come down to give and take in the aftermath of a seemingly potential disaster. No one in the family will be quite the same again. There is a real danger that family members will blame each other for problems that are, in fact, caused by a serious illness. Carers may feel that sufferers are not pulling their weight at a time when such an attitude is just not reasonable. Equally, sufferers may bitterly resent being dependent to some extent on others and blame them for their almost intolerable predicament. It is important to remember at these times that the sufferer's spouse, parent or child did not *want* to become a carer and did not plan such a role any more than the sufferer planned to have an illness.

Although the term 'carer' has tended to be abused, even stigmatized, it is worth remembering that the existence of a carer does imply that someone does care and, however frustrating the circumstances, most of us really do have a need for someone to care about us, don't we? It may help a little to bear in mind that it can be very distressing to watch someone you love devastated by an illness. Both sufferer and carer are in pain. Both can support each other and put the blame where it should lie, with the illness, as it is the illness that has given them these unwelcome and unexpected roles.

We shall come back to some of these and other problems later in the book. Meanwhile let's now take a look at how it feels to have someone in your family suffer with a severe mental illness.

Part II   The Impact on the family

6

Reactions and important relationships

Perhaps there can be nothing more devastating than to find someone you love becoming a stranger in front of your eyes and that, try as you may, apparently you can do nothing about it.

The anguish of the concerned onlookers

This is a common experience for the relatives of someone developing a serious mental illness They are likely to watch a loved one acting in an unfamiliar, even bizarre, way and to despair of finding a way to do anything about this.

With schizophrenia or severe depression, the sufferer will probably withdraw from the outside world, retreating into the home and yet keeping the family at bay, watching helplessly. On the other hand, with the onset of a manic illness, the family may be alarmed by a bewildering restlessness and recklessness and find that tentative attempts to caution or restrain their relative are met with hostility.

In each type of illness, there will probably be changed sleeping patterns – either pronounced insomnia or an upturning of the body's 24-hour clock – with the individual sleeping during the day and prowling the house most of the night. They may see other behaviour that relates to the sorts of symptoms discussed in Chapter 2. We know these can involve the individual in all sorts of scary and isolating experiences. There may be withdrawal and distrust, even within the comparative safety of the family home. In particular, the sufferer may well be developing paranoid ideas about close members of the family – invariably these focus on those who matter most to the individual. This can be the cause of much hurt and unhappiness, which can then be exacerbated by any mental health workers who either do not understand or choose to deny this phenomenon.

A state of chaos

Either way, more often than not the family will find themselves shut off and unable to get through to this stranger in their midst. They know something is desperately wrong, but, initially, they have no idea what is the matter. Later, many will accurately define the problem as some sort of mental illness, long before the experts will acknowledge this because the system is geared towards a 'let's wait and see' policy, with everyone waiting for something to happen. All too often, this 'something' may be a potentially disastrous crisis situation. Meanwhile, families may be left in ignorance about what is happening, as it is quite common for professionals to offer no explanations at this stage. Perhaps it is not too surprising that some professionals talk about 'mad families' as by the time the services involve themselves in the problem, some relatives are at breaking point and beginning to believe that they or the rest of the world have gone quite mad!

Over the years, I have lost count of the number of times families have come to me after the event with 'You won't believe what has happened to us'. Not only would I believe it, I'd be more or less word perfect on the story about to unfold, so often have I heard it before – a story of ignored pleas for help, of withheld information and of unpardonable delays.

Becoming battle weary

As we have seen, acknowledgement, diagnosis and treatment are sometimes obtained at a time of crisis. In many cases, they follow only after the family has become proactive and insisted on a proper service and, all too often, after damage has already been done to important relationships. At this point, the members of the family will not only be battle weary, they will almost certainly be profoundly exhausted.

On top of this, they will feel guilty and at fault in some way, particularly if their relative has been forced to go into hospital in order to get the treatment and care so urgently needed. They will also be feeling anxious and frightened for the future, unsure whether or not their spouse, son or daughter, brother or sister will ever be the same again, able to resume a normal life.

Their minds will be spinning with unspoken and unanswered questions. Should they have acted differently? Is this all their fault anyway? Have they lost the familiar personality of someone dear to them for ever? Can they cope if things *don't* ever return to normal? If the illness continues, what effect will this have on everyone's lives? Why has this happened to them?

Even at this point there may seem to be no one with whom they can talk honestly, with each family member instinctively protecting the others from further upset.

Disempowerment

Unless they are fortunate enough at this stage to benefit from information and guidance from someone who can appreciate the extent of these feelings of devastation, the family may remain damaged indefinitely by what was happened.

Again and again, relatives ask why they were given no real explanations nor help in finding a way forward at this time. Frequently, individual family members whose lives may never be the same again have no contact whatever with the mental health professionals concerned with the sufferer's treatment. The ignorance experienced by so many relatives leads to feelings of helplessness and confusion. The secrecy and denial that surrounds the handling of serious mental illness leads to disempowerment of the very individuals who are most important to the sufferer's survival. This ignorance deprives families of the coping mechanisms we all draw on at times of crisis.

Until they can access vital information about this type of illness – and there is plenty available – families may flounder and stumble along, having to learn by trial and error. This is undermining for them and unhelpful for the sufferer.

Violence in the home

Sometimes, even with a first, and perhaps only, episode of a psychotic illness, things may have been allowed to reach the critical stage where a family member moves away and shuns the family home. This happened to Jean's family when her younger son, Bob, became tormented by an unrecognised schizophrenic illness.

Bob

Even while their mother was out of the house trying, yet again, to get help for him, neighbours were unable to drag Bob off his brother, John, before he had half-strangled him.

These two young men had always got on well and had both shared a responsibility, as they saw it, for looking after their widowed mother. Bob's attack had been associated with paranoid ideas that his brother had become evil and was intending to harm Jean. This incident with his brother resulted in the sufferer's belated admission to hospital and subsequent recovery.

Before Bob returned home, John moved out of the family home and left no forwarding address. This close little family was destroyed by their ignorance about a common and treatable illness. No counselling took place and no one explained about paranoia and how it usually focuses on the relationships that matter most to the sufferer.

Clearly, John didn't understand that his brother's illness had made him behave this way. In fact, no one gave John any of the explanations he needed to find a way forward within a loving family.

Although such incidents of violence in the home are not common, there are too many that result from untreated symptoms of psychosis while mental health professionals wait for evidence that sufferers are a danger to themselves or others. Yet this is not even a requirement of the law – we shall come back to this vexing subject in Chapter 10.

Fortunately, most families survive this type of trauma, but it has to be said that few of the individuals concerned forget the horror of a violent incident and all say that the fear returns instantly with any signs of relapse, however many years later this may occur. All have been badly let down by the system, but none more so than those who are left in ignorance as to why the violence occurred.

Embarrassment

A more frequent result of waiting for something to happen is the very real risk of the sort of bizarre behaviour that can seriously affect the sufferer's future social standing in the community and can also have a spin-off effect on other family members.

Teenagers are particularly vulnerable in this respect, be they brothers, sisters or children of a sufferer whose behaviour has become bizarre to the point that neighbours and acquaintances become aware of this. Young people wish only to be part of the crowd, to be just like their friends and not to attract unwanted attention. They can therefore find it excruciatingly painful to have one of the family attracting adverse attention, particularly as there is sadly such a stigma attached to mental illness. They may find it difficult to forgive their relative for attracting attention to themselves, as they see it.

It is really very important that they should be given enough information to enable them to have some understanding of what has been happening to the sufferer. When this is achieved, some young people become remarkably supportive and, in doing so, discover that others in their age group can be particularly accepting of mental illness if given the chance.

A daughter's perspective

Perhaps more significant than any feeling of embarrassment is the burden of responsibility that some children – grown up or otherwise – assume when a parent is ill, as Kim did.

Kim

Kim's mother suffered six acute depressive episodes leading up to the time of her menopause. A normally lively and forceful personality, she had no previous problems with her health and her three daughters were shocked when she became ill. Although Kim quickly dismisses the suggestion that she took on most of the burden of care while her mother was ill, it is clear that it was she who tended to be at home with her mother during these bouts of depression. She was 14 years of age when these started and, four years later, became the main carer when her father left home.

During most of that time, Kim keenly remembers that no one talked with her and her sisters about their mother's illness – they were left to somehow find the resources to help her as best they could. She says 'it would have been great to have had someone to turn to at the worst times, so long as they didn't come in to tell us what we should and should not do, but were prepared to listen to our experience and offer some encouragement and appreciation of how we were feeling'. Kim feels that the responsibility would have been overwhelming without her sisters to turn to and talk with. She does not understand how an only son or daughter could possibly manage without this sort of back-up, but realises they are often left to do just that.

She remembers sometimes dreading walking into the house when she knew her mother was depressed, but feeling that something terrible would happen if she or one of her sisters were not there for her. She quite soon learned to feel guilty if she found herself starting to enjoy herself when she was out of the house. On the other hand, there were times when she despaired of battling on, facing hours of trying to cope with her mother's agitation and looking for ways to calm her fears. Even when she came out of these episodes, Kim was fearful that her mother would lose the job that meant so much to her and to which she invariably seemed to return too soon, each time pre-empting fears of failure.

Kim eventually went off to college, but she found herself reluctantly returning home every other weekend during the first term and she felt separated from other students by the worry and embarrassment of an illness she felt unable to talk about. However, Kim says now 'it was an experience that made me have more understanding of other people's problems; it was not a bad thing to have gone through'.

Eventually, her mother recovered and remarried and Kim explains with wonder that she found it quite difficult to adjust to a normal lifestyle at this time, not really being able to 'let go'. For a couple of months, she found she was very emotional and anxious to be alone, but eventually this normally sociable young woman learned to relax and feel it was OK to get on with living her own life. Someone else was in charge now; Kim could be a daughter again! Later she and her mother were to enjoy a mutually rewarding friendship.

A parent's perspective

Except in those fortunate cases where sufferers can eventually get on with their lives as if nothing important had happened, many young people will have to come to terms with giving up at least some of their hopes and plans for the future. As we know, some will never fulfil their original potential and, tragically, a small minority will not achieve very much at all. Clearly, this can be a cruel fate for the sufferer, particularly where there is acute awareness of former dreams and of losing them. It is not so obvious just how devastating this can also be for those close to the individual, particularly for their parents.

Even sadder is the predicament some families find themselves in when a really debilitating schizophrenic illness has robbed them of the familiar personality they knew and loved, as happened to Marian's son.

Jeff
Marian's son, Jeff, still matters very much to her and her husband and they continue to devote much of their time to making sure his quality of life is as rewarding as they can make it. However, if Marian is asked how it feels to have this happen to you, she refers to the ongoing unresolved bereavement with which they and others like them have to cope. She explains that however much she still cares about Jeff and however much she adapts and adjusts to reality rather than to what might have been, the original personality she knew and loved for so many years is gone, apparently for ever.

Jeff *looks* much the same but he is *not* the same; he is entirely different because the negative symptoms have taken their toll. Thus, the bereavement is unresolvable and the pain doesn't lessen. Fifteen years later, she still has tears in her eyes when she talks of this pain and the guilt she feels for even acknowledging these raw feelings of loss.

A husband's perspective

Perhaps of all the family it is a sufferer's spouse who has to make the most adjustment. While many marriages will survive a serious mental illness, some of these will provoke special problems for the well partner, particularly where there are young children. There may be a need to be mother *and* father, as well as carer, at least at times of relapse.

Dick

Dick used to cope well enough most of the time, but found that when his wife relapsed, she particularly needed him at just the time when he should be giving his time to their two little boys, who naturally missed their mother.

She had five manic breakdowns over a nine-year period and he soon learned to see these coming, but could not make her or the doctors listen to him. 'Just before she "goes", she changes completely', he told me. 'It is like having a jug of ice-cold water chucked in your face. Wouldn't you think it would save everyone trouble and expense if someone would do something before she runs amoke each time?'

Instead, he found himself trying to hold down a job, while rushing from work to home to the hospital each day, only to find that his wife was starting divorce proceedings, yet again, because she became paranoid about him when she was ill. Worse, sometimes hospital staff seemed to be encouraging this! He described his life as a 'mixture of heaven and hell', but was quite sure that the family could have been spared some of the worst moments if those who could help would have listened and taken note of what had happened before each occasion his wife became ill. 'It was like they had never heard of us each time it happened!', he marvelled. 'Wouldn't you think they'd want to stop the kids having to go through this again and again?' Yes, I would.

A wife's perspective

For the wife whose husband becomes mentally ill, there may be a need for more profound adjustments. For example, society still tends to expect the 'man of the house' to be the provider and all that goes with it.

Sarah

Sarah used to be the sort of wife who liked to share her everyday problems with her husband and to feel she could lean on him if she needed to.

She married a successful sales executive and had no idea that he had suffered a mild breakdown several years before he met her. He and his parents had been assured this was a 'one off' episode of no consequence. Sadly, his second breakdown damaged him and he could no longer pursue his sales career. Eventually he gave up working after attempting to cope with several part-time jobs.

Unable to sell their home because of negative equity problems, Sarah has had to resume her own career while their two children are still very young and to become 'all things to all people', as she puts it. She is responsible for paying the mortgage, for looking after the home and the children and for protecting the man she married from their demands for attention and from any need to mix with other people whenever he is particularly vulnerable. Even seeing a neighbour in the garden or going into a local shop is too stressful for him at such times.

Sarah is too busy to spend much time musing about what has happened to them, but she has her moments of despair. Most of all she misses the intimate companionship that was previously such an important part of the couple's relationship. She sometimes feel she has lost the man she married when he is beset with delusional fears. These have not really responded to currently available medication and Sarah is hoping that one of the increasingly sophisticated drugs becoming available will eventually help her husband. Meanwhile, she is ashamed that she has the odd moment when she finds herself almost hating him for what has happened to them both.

Living one day at a time

Most families having to cope with an ongoing serious mental illness, rather than a rare acute episode, comment ruefully that they can never be sure of anything again – tomorrow can always turn into a minefield!

Those closest to someone with a psychotic illness must come to terms with living with this uncertainty, with keeping an ever-watchful eye, with taking responsibility for stepping in, even though the sufferer may resent this. Those who have had an experience like John had with his brother Bob but, unlike him, have stayed within the family, will be particularly diligent in watching for a possible relapse. Where a paranoid illness exists, they quickly learn that the paranoia tends to focus back on the same individual(s) each time, despite the resumption of a probably rewarding relationship in between times.

Whatever the problems, many families *do* stay together and would not want to contemplate doing otherwise. This is just as well as few sufferers gain from finding themselves isolated in a seemingly uncaring world. We all need our families when we are vulnerable and no one should have to cope with a severe mental illness on their own. As a general rule, families break down either because they are left in ignorance of what has happened to them, as in John's case, or because they are left to cope with one crisis too many and all the trauma that goes with it.

Don't let this happen to you – insist on explanations and an effective service from those who are trained and paid to provide it. Meanwhile, let's take a look at how the family can help itself and find ways of moving forward.

7

Moving forward together

I believe that the first priority for everyone in the family is to accept that no one is to blame for what has happened. The real culprit is an illness, one that might have picked on *any* member of any family.

As we have seen, psychosis has a way of bringing chaos and strife to all those involved with its victims as well as to the victims themselves. Features of breakdown, such as uncertainty about the future, uninhibited and unpredictable behaviour, paranoia and unwanted dependency on others, can cause bitterness and resentment among the very people who should be united in fighting a common enemy rather than each other. No one wants to be ill nor to be dependent on others, however temporarily. Similarly, no one has asked to become a carer and to feel obliged to keep a protective eye on another adult who may see this as in intrusion. Everyone wants to get on with their lives – being parents, husbands or wives, and brothers or sisters – not take on the unexpected role of being a 'sufferer' or a 'carer', with all that these roles entail.

In other words, everyone in the family needs the help and support of other family members if the illness is not to 'divide and rule' and lead to despair and self-recriminations and little else. To appreciate the full meaning of this, consider for a moment how it must feel to be one of John's family (whose tragedy we discussed in Chapter 6), since he fled the home without trace.

A need to opt out?

It may be, of course, that a member of your family will feel the need to withdraw partially, or completely, from the situation. This may well turn out to be a temporary need – a need for respite – and represent a practical way forward for that particular individual to deal with an unresolved trauma. Meanwhile, it does not have to lead to family breakdown if everyone can accept what is happening and focuses on making sure that no irreversible step is taken at such a time and no doors are closed forever.

Mutual respect

It could be said that no marriage or family can function well unless we take care to remember to treat each other with respect, whatever life may bring. This is particularly true when a family is trying to support a relative through a psychotic illness. As we saw in the last chapter, all those close to a sufferer can be affected and every one will need to know that any positive contribution they make is appreciated, not taken for granted, by the rest of the family. In particular, it is most important to recognise any special effort or slight progress made by your relative who is having to cope personally with at least some of the experiences we discussed in Chapter 2. As we all know, a little appreciation and encouragement can go a long way and they are also a way of showing our respect.

A joint effort

If the illness persists, then it may well be that one member of the family will have more to give than others – often this will be a mother or spouse. However, some input from everyone will be far more valuable to the sufferer, and the family as a whole, than anything approaching martyrdom on the part of one member alone. This last situation is undesirable and creates two victims of the illness instead of one. At worst, where a sufferer's illness is ongoing and incapacitating, it can eventually lead to the depressingly familiar phenomenon of a lone carer, the rest of the family having deserted them, this person having been martyred, in fact, by an illness that has been allowed to take this terrible toll.

Identifying needs

In finding a way forward, it is essential to identify the priorities for each member of the family and, perhaps, to make a few 'house rules' that mean everyone's needs are catered for. A positive acceptance of the illness is only possible if it is not allowed to encroach too far on the lives of all concerned, so we will return to this subject later in the chapter.

The sufferer's needs

Let's start with the need of sufferers to be acknowledged as the victims of a serious illness. If we accept that this is the case, then we give them the dignity of a no-nonsense 'sick role' for as long as this is appropriate and we avoid becoming judgemental and critical in a way that can be destructive. Let's take a look now at some of the features of a serious mental illness that can lead to friction and frustration.

The lack of motivation in a chronic schizophrenic illness

Perhaps one of the most common complaints mental health workers hear from relatives of sufferers is 'but, he sits around all day, staring into

67

space, doing nothing!' May used to find this markedly irritating in her clearly able-bodied son.

May

She would come in from work hoping that he may have peeled the potatoes for the evening meal as requested, only to find that he had not even washed up his breakfast dishes. In fact, he showed no signs of having moved since she had left home that morning!

It took some time to persuade May that this would not change unless she allowed a few extra minutes each morning to motivate him. For example, starting the washing-up with her son and asking him to finish drying the dishes before sitting down with his next cup of coffee. She tried this and on her return home in the evenings, she would get him to count out some potatoes for her to peel while she put on the kettle. He would then make a pot of tea so that they could sit down together while his mother recharged her batteries before she prepared the rest of the meal and he laid the table.

Sometimes, May felt able to encourage him to help her with more cumbersome tasks, such as turning a mattress and changing the sheets or helping her mow the lawn or do some weeding. May has learned that she cannot expect her son to take the initiative or to get on with a task on his own – she has to provide the get up and go – and she also has to remind herself that there are some days when he is really not up to even this modest amount of exercise. However, she and her son have both been rewarded now by a mutual sense of shared achievement that is replacing the old feelings of frustration and resentment.

A similar problem in a depressive illness

It is worthy of note that lethargy and apathy in a depressive illness is unlikely to respond to even a gentle prod of the kind May gave her son. Chances are that attempts made by carers to motivate someone who is severely depressed will probably not succeed. If *your* relative is depressed, then it may help to accept that this sort of approach may not work and so spare yourself unnecessary feelings of failure and frustration. However, you can take heart from the knowledge that this depression should be temporary, unlike a chronic schizophrenic illness.

A 'lifeline' relationship in an acute schizophrenic illness

A special feature of an acute schizophrenic illness can be a peculiarly clinging relationship, with the sufferer using the mother or other individual as a lifeline around the time of breakdown through to complete recovery. The relationship can be very possessive and resemble that of a young child's towards its mother in that there may be a marked tendency to follow her around all the time. The situation can be quite worrying and frustrating for the mother, who will almost certainly mourn the time when her son or daughter did not need and rely on her in this way.

If this is happening to you, it may help to know that this relationship normalises again as the illness fades. Meanwhile, do all you can to encourage the sufferer to relate to others as well. Indeed, it would be a good idea to discuss this with other members of the family, too, as they may feel 'shut out' and even resented by the sufferer while the dependency lasts.

A craving for certain foods

We looked earlier at this fairly common phenomenon and it is one that can occur until the psychosis has waned in a manic or schizophrenic illness. One MD sufferer I know used to eat six bananas at a go between meals and, not surprisingly, found this led to a weight problem. More usually, the cravings lead to the consumption of amazing amounts of ice-cream, chocolate and other sweet or stodgy foods, at the expense of a healthily balanced diet.

This interesting, but largely neglected, feature of psychosis in some individuals can become a cause of concern as these sorts of eating habits can be very costly and escalate any tendency in some individuals for their prescribed medicines to encourage weight-gain. The eating of the craved foods merely triggers off more craving of the same and, in some cases, this can become so severe that any resemblance of table manners, or even allowing others at the table a share of these types of food, becomes a thing of the past.

As I mentioned in Chapter 4, I have persuaded sufferers in this predicament (always with the help of their families!) to move towards a diet less dependent on the sorts of refined carbohydrates that aggravate the craving. I'm afraid this requires some sacrifice from the rest of the family, too, as, after all, it is not reasonable to expect someone to diet if forbidden foods are readily available in the kitchen. The menu needs to be as tempting as you can make it, with ample proteins, fruit and vegetables, backed up with nutritious starches, such as baked jacket potatoes or brown rice, possibly avoiding cereals that contain gluten (see my book *Schizophrenia: A fresh approach* which may be available in your public library – more details in the Further reading section at the back of the book). It is a good idea to include several treats in the menu as well – few of us persevere with diets we find punitive!

All of this calls for considerable effort by all concerned and the chef is quite likely to find various members of the family (including the focus of the exercise) chomping away on forbidden foods in the nearest public eating place. Do keep at it, though, for perhaps a month or so initially, if there's enough goodwill in the household as a diet like this can do wonders for *everyone's* figure as well as provide plenty of nutrients.

Changed sleeping pattern

Any tendency for one person to be up and about during the night while others are trying to sleep is quite disrupting in most households. As we have noted, many schizophrenia sufferers experience an upturning of their 24-hour clock and come to life late in the evening and eventually fall into bed not long before the rest of the household has to get up next morning. Similarly, a relative in a mildly manic phase may be up and about all night, after, say, an hour's refreshing sleep, and chatter away on the telephone to other night owls or even decide to wake you or other members of the family with news of some exciting new plan conceived in the dead of night. Others might decide to listen to loud music instead!

It is not, anyway, conducive to relaxing and getting a sound sleep if you are worried about the restless person lighting a cigarette and perhaps leaving it to burn merrily away or putting the kettle on and then forgetting about it, which does happen. Similarly, it is not reassuring to know that your relative may stroll out of the house for a while, perhaps leaving the front door open. Most of all, there is little hope of sleep if the television is turned on loudly or if you are conscious of the soft boom boom of a favourite CD.

This whole problem can be so potentially destructive for everyone in the household that it usually needs to be dealt with under a house rule, and we will come back to this later.

Self-neglect

Not only can sufferers have trouble with their eating and sleeping patterns, but some also lose interest in their appearance and hygiene. This may be a feature of either a schizophrenic or a depressive illness and is often only temporary, but it is a feature that nevertheless tends to cause considerable friction in the home.

The best way to tackle this is to find some sort of compromise that precludes nagging by the family in exchange for a promise to take a shower or bath on a regular, albeit minimal, basis, as well as putting everything one is wearing into the family laundry basket at those times! In some cases, this is another matter that eventually becomes the subject of a house rule, of which more later.

Paranoid ideas

Any persistence of delusional thoughts, particularly if these include any residual paranoid feelings about other members of the household, can be a problem for everyone.

At this point, it may be worth while looking at reality testing again in Chapter 4 and making an ongoing contract similar to the one discussed there between sufferer and carer. This will only be feasible if those involved are prepared to to make this sort of commitment. As I warned earlier, this is hard work but it can contribute to the sufferer having a better grip on reality and making a more complete recovery. It can also mean that interested family members can help in a really practical way while gaining more insight into the persistence and torment of a delusional illness. This can form the basis of a rewarding working partnership, too.

Grandiose ideas

One of the most difficult features of an MD illness can be a tendency for sufferers to have residual grandiose ideas and to tend to be impatient with those around them – not suffering fools gladly, as they, but not others, may see it! For the time that this sort of supreme confidence lingers, it may be better to refrain from reacting in any way. However, if a comment is called for, then it would be appropriate to say, quietly but firmly, something like, 'I do see that that is what you believe at the moment, but this is not how I see it'. Such a statement can help to define reality without being unnecessarily abrasive.

Coping with rapid changes of moods

It can be unnerving and distressing to never be sure how you'll find your relative from hour to hour.

John and Beth

John used to find this very difficult. His wife's rapid mood swings frequently escalated into real highs and her doctors had great difficulty in finding the right maintenance medication for her illness. Increasingly, this couple, who had been ideally happy together for the ten years prior to Beth's breakdown, became virtual enemies during the bad times. The good times were spoilt by recriminations over Beth's spending sprees and other nightmare scenarios in which she became involved.

Eventually, when the couple realised what was happening, they took time out to talk about this during one of Beth's calmer periods and to agree a strategy for protecting their money and to stop her whirling off in the car for hours on end. For what seemed to them to be an eternity, John managed to hold things together while Beth waited for more effective treatment. They have been rewarded since by a marriage that is better than ever as a result of the ordeal they have survived together. Theirs was not a typical experience because Beth's problems were quite extreme for a long time, but it may be a timely reminder that things can work out well in the end, even if they do seem desperate during the bad times.

Avoiding collusion with a core delusion

As we have noted, when sufferers are psychotic, they believe this is not the case. It is as if the function of this core delusion, as I call it, is to perpetuate the illness. It presents the main obstacle to obtaining help at a time of crisis and it also provides a good reason for coming off medication once the crisis seems to have been resolved. At this point, it is very common for sufferers to protest that they would now be completely well if it wasn't for the medication!

If this happens with your relative, then the rest of the family can best help by first ensuring that any concerns or problems regarding possible side-effects are discussed fully with involved professionals. Beyond that, it is important not to be tempted to believe that your relative is 'drugged up', but, rather, they are suffering from the typical symptoms of the first stages of recovery from a breakdown. The medication has more than one function. Not only does it serve to bring the sufferer out of a psychotic nightmare, but it also, in many cases, helps keep the illness at bay afterwards. Do remember this and encourage your relative to persevere with the treatment. Once he or she regains a firm grip on reality and gradually becomes involved in a day-to-day routine, then – and only then – will any outward signs and feelings of being 'drugged up' disappear.

This is really just one part of a bigger problem that faces some families trying to cope with a serious mental illness in the home. It can be tempting, or even seem prudent in some cases, to collude with your relative in denying any returning signs of illness. It may therefore be a good idea to make a house rule right from the start that any signs of relapse in the sufferer, or refusal to accept treatment, will be discussed openly with involved professionals. Sometimes, relatives or other carers feel pressurised and restrained by feelings of loyalty when needing outside help, so it can be helpful to make a clear statement from the beginning on this important issue so that all know where they stand. Later, sufferer and family may be able to work on this together by identifying any specific warning signs of relapse and agreeing with professionals on how help can be obtained as and when needed (there is further discussion of this matter in Chapter 11).

Other family members have needs too!

It cannot be overemphasised just how important this is.

Archie
I corresponded for a while with Archie, a family man who was trying very hard 'not to run', as he put it – hard not to forsake a wife he loved and wanted to spend the rest of his life with.

This was becoming increasingly difficult because, with each of several relapses following a gradual rejection of medication, his schizophrenic stepson became resentful of his presence. Archie was becoming more and more polarised by the sufferer's aggressive determination to monopolise his mother's attention and to exclude the stepfather he used to relate to well. Archie's wife found herself colluding more and more with her son's forceful demands and, by the time he wrote to me, Archie was becoming certain that the next relapse would be one too many. He summed up his predicament with the words, 'there has to be a regime which allows for all those who are long-term participants in the drama to continue with an acceptable level of compromise to their personal needs. If the demands on any one are too great, then breakdown of the group will occur'. Sadly, this fact of life has been ignored for too long by most of those who work with serious mental illness.

Identifying needs

If a family is to survive, then there must be an opportunity for its individual members to be honest about their feelings. Once help is available for a first psychotic episode, then the rest of the family should sit down together and feel free to express any fears and doubts they may have about being able to cope. This can lead to regular family conferences about practical issues and the sufferer can take part in these later on if and when he or she is well enough to do so without feeling stressed. These conferences can be used for tackling any problems that have arisen and for drawing up new house rules if, and as, the need arises.

House rules – some examples

The sorts of matters that usually come up for discussion when considering house rules can be divided into those that are relevant to a sufferer's recovery and quality of life and those that are relevant to the rest of the family's needs, although there will, of course, be an overlap between the two. For example, turning day into night is completely beyond the sufferer's control, so it is unfair, as well as unproductive, for other family members to grumble or nag about this. However, it is not beyond the sufferer's control to refrain from *acting* as if the night is daytime by avoiding playing loud music, clattering crockery, banging doors or generally making enough noise to keep others in the household awake. Also, it can be helpful to gradually work at changing the pattern in so far as this is possible. So, in Bill's household – where lack of sleep was leading to a state of war – a compromise had to be found and a house rule was agreed which read something like this.

- The family will not grumble and complain about Bill's need to be up and about during the night.
- Bill will not make the sorts of noises that wake others up. For instance, if he wants to play music or listen to the radio, he will keep the sound right down or use ear plugs.
- No one will nag Bill to get up in the mornings. He agrees to his mother waking him up at noon on three weekdays when he will come downstairs for a meal.

This worked so well that eventually Bill's mother was able to persuade him to start going to a drop in centre on one of these three days and this in turn was such a success that he now chooses to go to the centre on four days in the week and sleeps far less in the day than he used to. Importantly, this satisfactory state of affairs was only achieved after several months of determined effort and it depended on a good-humoured approach by all members of the family, including Bill.

In Archie's case, a similar approach could almost certainly have stopped the rot setting in. His stepson's monopolisation of his wife became tyrranical and this focused on his wanting to get rid of the third person in the house – Archie's presence was resented. Making several house rules might have helped to right the situation, but it is more probable that a contract would have been required to cover the following issues.

- Archie and his wife to have time and space to themselves that is appropriate to their being man and wife.
- Archie's wife to use her influence in a positive way, to encourage her son to get involved in some sort of activity outside of the home several times a week with the help of the local mental health services.
- The son to take his medication regularly.

- Bullying behaviour of any kind not to be tolerated.

It would be necessary for the terms of the contract to be a condition of the son's continuing to live in the parental home. Almost certainly, the family would have needed professional or other skilled help in order to change direction in this way, but this in itself would alert the local mental health services to the seriousness of the situation.

Sufferers themselves will, of course, sometimes feel the need to establish certain rights. Some of these may require to be covered by a house rule and several I have seen have included a taboo on nagging by family members and acknowledgment by the family of the individual's right, and need, for ample privacy and space.

Really, it all comes down to give and take and the making of clear boundaries we all need to ensure this is achieved.

Summing up

We have looked at several strategies that have helped some families to cope with a serious mental illness in the home. None of this is as simple and straightforward as this brief discussion might seem to be trying to suggest. However, with enough determination and a large measure of good humour, this kind of approach can provide a basis for moving forward and may be adopted to each family's own particular needs and strengths. If you and yours are trying to find a way forward, why not give this a try?

8

Coping with the outside world

The nature of a family's relationships with the outside world suddenly assumes enormous importance once one of its members is struck down with a serious mental illness. Even while families are stretching out and pleading for help from professionals, they may be withdrawing from the rest of society.

A reluctant but voluntary isolation

If you have been there, you will know that this sort of instinctive response by the family may begin to happen long before a diagnosis and treatment are available due to the sorts of delays that so often occur. Your relative's reactions and behaviour may have been causing concern for some time and the likelihood is that the family will have turned in on itself in a desperate effort to cover up the sick relative's predicament. Because society tends to deny the existence of serious mental illness instead of recognising it for what it is, most families feel they have to protect the sufferer from earning a reputation associated with marked stigma, fear and ignorance. This can be so real that it is quite natural for the family to become defensive about the problem, fiercely protecting their relative from potential ruin as they see it.

Perhaps the easiest way to identify with this common reaction is to remember that we are talking about something that, above all, affects the future of the one person who is not in a position to do anything about it at this time. The rest of the family have no way of knowing how much information their sick relative would want to share with others when well again. As a rule, we do not go about broadcasting to all and sundry the affairs of those we love and we would certainly draw the line at passing on information that could seriously prejudice their chances of getting on with their lives. Well, this is precisely the predicament that many families find themselves facing. They feel a need to protect their sick relative's right to privacy until such time as it becomes clear whether or not the illness will be ongoing and severe enough to make hiding it an impossibility or of a temporary nature. If the latter turns out to be the case, then their recovered relative will be able to make the decision about whether or not to 'come out' about the illness or, perhaps, just to share what has happened with a trusted few, as and when the need occurs.

I have come across several instances where sufferers have been able to eventually resume their usual lifestyle without having been *publicly* labelled and without any damage having been done to their social life or career plans. There can be little doubt that, at the present time, this would be a central aim of many potentially well sufferers and those close to them.

Too high a cost?

More often, though, things don't work out quite like this and then the cost of protecting their relative may well seem to have been too high for the rest of the family. By instinctively building a protective wall around their relative, family members isolate themselves and, reluctantly, have to forfeit the right to the support they need so much at such a time. This can be a real sacrifice when their everyday life may be turning into a nightmare and when home feels more like a potential minefield than a sanctuary. Most of us need to talk about what is happening to us and seek help and comfort from our friends when we are confused and unhappy. At the very least, it can help if friends and work colleagues know what is happening to us, what we are experiencing and why we are finding life so difficult. It is very hard for stressed families to forego this sort of moral support, but it happens all the time.

It is a sacrifice even sufferers themselves often remain unaware of. Indeed, when the 'family theories' of psychotic illness were fashionable, professionals used to consider the unnatural isolation of so many of 'those families' to be a typical feature of their inability to function normally within society – taking it to be the sort of thing that may have contributed to the sufferer having a schizophrenic illness. So, there was little comfort to be had from the so-called experts while such theories were pre-dominant either.

Building bridges

If all of this is familiar to you and your family, then you will have realised at some point how important it is to start building bridges again into the larger community. It is inevitable, of course, that some relatives, friends or neighbours may become significant by their absence when they do learn what is wrong. However, it helps to remember that fair-weather friends eventually show their true colours at some time or other. They should be the last of your problems at this stage. It is far more important to concentrate on more worthwhile relationships that may have been temporarily abandoned during the family's trauma.

The role of relatives and close reltives

The safest place to start is probably with the rest of the family and with close friends, if this has not been possible before and if the sufferer is happy about this.

You might start by sharing any simple explanations you have been able to obtain about the illness, particularly emphasising what it might be like to experience the illness from the *inside*. This will be particularly important if the sufferer has got into any sort of trouble while ill or is now tending to behave in an unfamiliar way. This sort of understanding makes it more likely that potentially supportive relatives and friends will meet the needs of an individual who has enough to contend with trying to come to terms with what has happened. We all need to be appreciated and respected and there is less chance of this happening while the sufferer is still vulnerable unless others are given a chance to identify at least in part, with how this must feel.

The right sort of support

If explanations are given in a positive, optimistic way, then there is a good chance that the sufferer may benefit from valuable and enthusiastic support, which can make it easier to develop a healthy daily routine in the early days of recovery. If others understand that the sufferer may be loathe to even leave the house at this stage, let alone get involved in mixing socially, then they can better appreciate how helpful it can be to have moral support and encouragement to go out for, say, a walk through the park, a short shopping expedition or a swim, any of which may be reasonably attractive so long as one has an agreeable companion to go with! This sort of support on a regular basis can do much to lead to the gradual resumption of a normal lifestyle.

Accessing the wider community

One big advantage for the family in being part of the larger community can be the helpful extra contacts that this may provide for a sufferer whose illness is persistent and who cannot hope to make the type of recovery that leads to returning to a completely independent life. I can think of one case that illustrates this particularly well.

Rodney
Since childhood, Rodney has lived with the experience of a close relative having a persistent schizophrenic illness. Sadly, eight years ago, one of his sons developed the illness in his mid-teens and has needed his family's support since that time.

Rodney's previous experience led to him taking an interest in youth work and he spends much of his spare time doing voluntary work. He is very aware of how much it matters to young people to find a meaningful role within the community, and how much more this applies to those who have to cope with a disability. Because of this he has encouraged his son to greet all-comers at the door, to answer the telephone and take messages on his behalf, and to take an interest in some of the activities Rodney and his colleagues arrange for teenagers in the neighbourhood.

The local community has responded in kind and several friends call at the house during the week to involve Rodney's son in the sorts of outings and activities he enjoys.

All this has led to the young man knowing that he belongs and matters in the wider community and to him enjoying the sort of rewarding life that he may otherwise have been denied.

Equally important, this sort of support would go a long way to making life more rewarding for the more socially isolated sufferers and carers who sometimes find themselves relying on each other's company to such an extent that this is to the detriment of an otherwise potentially good relationship. If this how it is for you, then it might be worth seeking help, perhaps with the aid of mental health workers, from a neighbourhood church or other local organisation that might provide a befriending service or opportunities for integrating more into the outside community. Why not give this a try?

Meeting other families

Perhaps a safe and reassuring way to start stretching out to the community beyond the household may be to make a determined effort to meet with others who have been there. If your family is battle weary and still licking its wounds after all the potential trauma of a psychotic crisis, then it can be encouraging to meet with others who have had the same sorts of experiences and are able to genuinely identify with what has happened to you. There is a further advantage to be gained as families who have been there can share with each other hard-earned expertise and ways of coping. Many sufferers and carers say that the time when they eventually learned about the diagnosis and, as a result of this, met with others who really knew what it meant to go through such an experience, was the point at which they started to feel more in control of what was happening to them. Certainly, feelings of isolation and that your family is different to others can be devastating on top of everything else that has gone before, but these are quickly relieved by meeting with other nice people who have felt the same at some point. Often, too, there is a level of expertise among fellow sufferers and carers that is hard to find elsewhere. One mother wrote recently that her local self-help group had been more help to her and her son than everything else put together.

Mental health workers may be able to introduce your family to others coping with a serious mental illness, if you request this. Otherwise, organisations such as the Manic Depression Fellowship and National Schizophrenia Fellowship can certainly do so. They should also be able to introduce you to local self-help groups as well as providing recommended reading lists and access to up-to-date research findings. (See the useful addresses section at the back of the book for their addresses.)

The individual who has to go it alone

Probably, this potential contact with other sufferers is even more important for the sufferer who is trying to manage without ready family support. Not only can this provide a potential source of moral support and a chance to share experiences and ways of coping, but meeting with fellow sufferers may provide an otherwise rare opportunity to talk about one's illness.

If this is how it is for you, then it may be important to consider how best you can make such contact with others. If you are well enough to return to work and have little energy left for anything beyond this, then it may be important to join a local group such as those run by Manic Depression Fellowship or Nationl Schizophrenia Fellowship members. These usually involve an evening meeting on a once-monthly basis, as well as receiving newsletters and information about study days and conferences.

If you are not working – at present, anyway – then it might be a good idea to get involved with a local day centre or drop in facility, either as a client or a voluntary worker (or even both) and local mental health workers should be able to help you do this. If not, it may be worth contacting one of the voluntary organisations listed at the back of this book (see the Useful addresses section).

In Chapter 4, we looked at ways in which MD sufferers in particular may benefit from having a small group of trusted individuals to watch for changes of mood and signs of relapse as well as provide friendship and support. Whatever your illness, though, you are likely to benefit from this sort of social network, albeit modest, as it can provide stimulation and friendship as well as someone to keep an eye on you when you are vulnerable. You may well find it rewarding to do much the same for a fellow sufferer as well!

Sometimes it can help to be able to mix with fellow sufferers for another reason, too. Because there is no need to fret or fume about whether or not to mention your illness and because others may talk about all sorts of aspects of having to cope with this, it can become much easier to come to terms with what has happened to you. To put the whole thing in perspective, there are at least two in every 100 of the population who have been there.

I believe that it is important that you have adequate support from the mental health services too. Anyone having to cope alone with a serious mental illness should have regular, ongoing, support from a mental health worker. We live in a world that operates on the 'if you don't ask, you don't get' principle. This is a pity as it puts the onus on you to be assertive and state your need for this support when you are assessed or are the subject of a community care plan. I know this is easier said than done, but every policy statement on serious mental illness during the past few years has emphasised the need to listen to sufferers, so go ahead and make sure you are listened to. Explain that you need someone to talk to and to listen to you and that you might sometimes appreciate advice about all sorts of things that can become a problem for someone in your position. Make it clear that this would help you find a way forward if that is what you feel. It is your right to request this sort of back-up service and to receive it.

Looking at an outside world that has changed

When we talk about coping with the outside world in the title of this chapter, we are talking about an outside world that can suddenly look very different to the one that sufferers and their families knew before the advent of serious mental illness. On the one hand, familiar people may become unfamiliar because of a sudden lack of spontaneity, because of anxiety and doubts about what to expect and how to behave. We have all experienced this when a familiar situation changes for whatever reason. On the other hand, unfamiliar people may suddenly become a part of one's life, people who, in the past, probably had no reason to have any contact with you and your family. We are talking here about a variety of mental health workers.

Coping with the experts

The idea that sufferers and their families may need to learn to 'cope with' any or all of these professionals may seem a little strange. Nevertheless, if you are struggling to get help for someone in your family who may be developing a serious mental illness, you may find it a completely new, unwelcome experience to be in a position where you have to plead for help for a loved one and to suddenly realise that, at any point in that illness, your whole family's future can hang in the balance on decisions made by professionals who may well be strangers to you.

Likewise, at times of pending crisis, it may come as a shock to find that your family is being assessed as though this was an everyday situation in your household when, in fact, you are the key participants in a nightmare. Having survived this, you may then find that the service being offered may not be the one you are seeking. Families invariably want the sort of help that promises to immediately protect their vulnerable relative – they want speedy preventive measures at times of danger. In contrast, the system is geared towards waiting for and responding to crisis situations, with most professionals working within such a framework.

This climate can lead to conflict at a time when those seeking help are themselves very vulnerable. The agitated pleas of families for speedy and preventive action may not be appreciated by professionals any more than their 'let's wait and see' attitude is appreciated by families. All in all, meeting with professionals at a time of crisis – the very crisis you have probably been trying desperately hard to avoid – is not the best basis for promoting confidence. You are now totally dependent on the services for an answer to your predicament and anything but a sensitive assessment in such circumstances can seem like a bruising intrusion.

It may help to be aware that it is just part and parcel of the current approach to dealing with a developing or recurring psychotic illness in the community. It is also, hopefully, just a precursor to obtaining the necessary treatment, as well as a diagnosis if it is a first-time episode.

Meanwhile, we will take a look, in the next three chapters, at things you need to know about the system in order to make this work for you and for your family.

Part III Practical issues

9

Typical mental health resources

Let's take a look now at the professionals who will, to a greater or lesser extent, become involved with sufferers and their families depending on the persistence and severity of the illness.

General practitioners (GPs)

Although not a mental health specialist, your GP is, in fact, the gateway to the whole range of available mental health services. This can be reassuring as this professional is more familiar and accessible to most of us than are other health workers. However, be warned, obtaining help in these circumstances where a serious mental illness is suspected – even from a known and trusted doctor – can be a great deal more difficult to negotiate than most of us might imagine. Things can be unexpectedly complicated. Initially, even if your relative may be persuaded to go and see your GP, the extent of the problem may not be recognised by the doctor in a first, short interview and, later, when losing touch with reason, your relative is unlikely to want to have anything to do with doctors or to accepte medical advice. Very often, therefore, it will be a parent or other relative who eventually seeks the help of a GP.

As we shall see in the next two chapters, some GPs feel that their hands are tied by the system and they can do nothing, but most will try to find some way of working within this framework. Not surprisingly, it has been my experience that sufferers and families who have the sympathetic and knowledgeable support of their GP from the start tend to fare better than those who don't. Even if there is little that can be done immediately, such support and some sort of explanatiaon about what is happening can make all the difference between being able to cope or feeling that everything is out of control.

Community psychiatric nurses (CPNs)

These nurses are trained to work with the mentally ill. Most will have worked in mental hospitals or modern psychiatric units before coming out into the community. Depending on local practice, CPNs are now tending to work as part of community mental health teams.

CPNs can provide the ideal link between medical supervision and a relatively independent life in the community for many long-term sufferers and they will often supervise and monitor medication, for example, particularly when this is prescribed as an injection.

Sufferers and carers frequently express satisfaction with the service and support they receive from CPNs, especially in those areas that provide continuity of service rather than a rapid turnover of staff.

Occupational therapists (OTs)

It used to be that those OTs who worked with the mentally ill worked largely within a hospital setting, but, nowadays, they are very much involved with rehabilitation work. For example, they may help ex-patients settle down in the community after a longish period in hospital and support them in their efforts to gradually adapt to some sort of routine and work towards an improved quality of life. I have known one dedicated OT to work over long periods of time with sufferers who have previously slipped through the net and ended up destitute, living on the streets, eventually and successfully rehabilitating them into a more comfortable, sheltered life; in some cases, reuniting them with members of their family.

OTs also run therapeutic groups in the community and some of these may be helpful for individuals recovering from a serious mental illness, particularly if the therapists appreciate the problems that psychosis can bring for MD and schizophrenia sufferers.

Social workers

Before the first of a series of reorganisations within social services departments starting in the early 1970s, a group of social workers called mental welfare officers used to be very much involved with individuals with a serious mental illness and their families. I know very elderly carers who still talk about the service they received from these seemingly knowledgeable and dedicated specialists.

Unfortunately, today's social workers have little opportunity to have any ongoing contact with the seriously mentally ill or their families. Even those who have extra training that qualifies them to work with the mental health legislation – approved social workers (ASWs – see Chapter 10 for further details) – tend to work in one-off crisis situations much of the time. They rarely have an opportunity to get to know sufferers in their everyday situation and this means that they may only see them when things are going wrong.

This is a serious flaw in a system where the most far-reaching function of the ASW's role is to assess whether or not a sufferer requires admission to hospital at such times, even though two specialist doctors may be recommending this. How can a stranger assess the extent of the abnormality of a situation without prior experience of what the *everyday* situation is, that is, all those other times when those closest to the sufferer are *not* urgently seeking help? As the situation is then further complicated by a psychotic illness distorting everything that is going on among the people in the situation being assessed, it is no wonder that unhelpful decisions and unnecessary delays are legend in these crisis situations.

Rather differently, other social workers may be involved in assessing the needs of your relative in a *non*-crisis situation if this is requested. Recent legislation has made provision for the needs of carers to be assessed, too, but only *at the same time* as the sufferer, and only if this is *requested.* I strongly recommend carers to take advantage of this new facility, both to make social workers more aware of what it means to live with a serious mental illness and to take advantage of any resources that may be available – (I refer to this matter again in Chapter 13).

Clinical psychologists

It is surprising that many of these professionals seem to have little to do with psychosis or to have any real knowledge of the problems of living with this type of illness, though they are, of course, qualified to work with sufferers. One senior practitioner has been heard on several occasions to comment in public on 'these families' and their need to make out that their schizophrenic relative has an *illness* and another explained to me a couple of years ago that delusional ideas never respond to antipsychotic medication (I was very glad this is not true). Others have written books suggesting that schizophrenia is a myth.

On the other hand, not only are there notable exceptions in the profession, with some clinical psychologist teams specialising in working with this type of illness, but these teams have also tended to take a lead nationally in making an invaluable contribution to improving the quality of life for sufferers and carers alike. Methods involved include pioneering training programmes to help sufferers and relatives to identify and recognise warning signs of relapse and, more recently a specially adapted cognitive therapy approach to help sufferers cope with hallucinations and delusional ideas, but also to see themselves and the world around them in a more positive light. The National Schizophrenia Fellowship Advice Line (see the Useful addresses section at the back of the book) can provide more details about the work of such practitioners.

Psychiatrists

At the time of writing, it is not clear if these key professionals are going to have an opportunity to adapt to, and make viable, a 'community care' approach to serious mental illness. Hard pressed for time and vital resources such as hospital beds, many continue to work mainly within formal and clinical settings, such as hospital wards and outpatient clinics. They tend to only see sufferers and families in their homes at a time of crisis, which is certainly not an everyday, normal, situation! In fact, families rarely see any more of psychiatrists today than they did in the past – which was very little at all – despite the advent of community care. Usually, relatives have to make an appointment to see the hospital doctor supervising the sufferer's treatment if they have questions to ask (who doesn't?) and all too often then find themselves in the unnatural and awesome environment of a ward-round, surrounded by professionals.

Despite such difficulties, much will depend on the skills and caring of the doctor supervising your relative's treatment and aftercare. Some psychiatrists are skilled and dedicated in their efforts to minimise any damage wrought by psychotic illness and you will have every reason to be grateful if your relative comes under the care of one of them. Similarly, some of these doctors keep an eye on what is happening to their patients by liaising closely with CPNs or other professionals who may visit the home, which is also very helpful.

Other resources

The professionals mentioned above and various other mental health workers should all be available within your local mental health services. Let's now take a look at daycare, residential and other resources that should also be accessible to individuals with a serious mental illness.

Mental health resource centres

If you have one of these in your locality, then it should include a drop in service for individuals seeking information about mental illness and, in particular, advice about a relative or friend who may be causing concern. The centre may be a base for one or more local mental health teams and there should be opportunities to speak with a health professional. It may be possible to access ongoing help directly from this source, although it is likely that you will need a referral from your GP. In any event it should be possible to obtain information as well as guidance on finding a way forward.

Mental hospitals and psychiatric units

At the time of writing, some of the large, Victorian mental hospitals are still functioning in part, but most of these are due to close around the end of the 1990s. Some still provide acute beds for short, crisis admissions – although there is an increasing shortage of these – as well as beds in what used to be called 'back wards' for those long-term patients who are unlikely to cope without 24-hour supervised accommodation. Gradually this sort of accommodation is being provided within the community and the remaining acute beds are being transferred to modern psychiatric units in general hospitals. Meanwhile, daycare for some out-patients is still available in some of the old mental hospitals and certainly in the new modern psychiatrist units.

Day hospitals

These can provide the same sorts of facilities as those provided by hospitals for in-patients, but they're just there for the day, or part of the day at a clinic-type set-up, not overnight. At a time of breakdown, this will only be practical if the sufferer is well enough to agree to attend on a daily basis and if relatives are happy about this and feel able to cope with this acute phase of the illness in the home. A day hospital place can also be used to speed up an in-patient's discharge from hospital, thus releasing a bed for another urgent admission.

Alternatively, day hospitals provide sessional therapies that are appropriate for individuals who need less support. In some cases, this may include sufferers coping with a psychotic illness in the community. However, some of these well-resourced institutions show a marked tendency to focus on individuals with a less serious illness. Whether this will change with the increasing pressures of community care and a competitive NHS remains to be seen.

Day centres

These may be run by Social Services departments or bodies in the private or voluntary sectors. Some may cater for various types of disability, although their staff teams rarely include health professionals.

The centres provide various structured activities and usually a different progrmme can be arranged for each individual, with the applicant attending for an initial interview so that a mutually acceptable programme can be arranged and reviewed every so often. Frequency of attendance will be influenced by the availability of places as much as by each individual's needs. Attending a day centre can be a very helpful way to adapt to and maintain some sort of routine if, and while, a sufferer is not able to work.

Drop in centres

These facilities are, more often than not, provided by voluntary organisations, such as local MIND groups and the National Schizophrenia Fellowship. Their friendly informality can be attractive to sufferers who need some stimulation and routine, but do not respond to more structured services and this is quite often the case with many individuals whose lifestyle is impaired by a severe mental illness. Self-referral is usually the order of the day, with clients coming and going as they please.

The best of these resources offer a chance to feel as if one belongs and matters. They offer a warm welcome, the company of others who have been there themselves and subsidised refreshments. Some offer a lot else besides, such as a variety of table games and snooker or pool and table tennis, as well as 'round the table' discussions, informal counselling and advice on benefits and other everyday issues.

While staff may be untrained (and some will be unpaid), they often have a special interest in, or experience of, severe mental illness, perhaps, in some cases, being carers or recovered sufferers themselves. Staff may keep an informed and friendly eye on their 'regulars' and increasingly there is an opportunity for the latter to become involved in the day-to-day policies and running of the resource, which can be both therapeutic and a boost to a frail ego!

One type of resource, known as the 'Clubhouse model', is now becoming popular. This provides the sort of drop in facility we have talked about here, but also provides opportunities for rehabilitating members into a work routine – and, where appropriate, may introduce them to jobs in the open market (always depending, of course, on the local employment situation).

Twenty-four-hour helplines and advocacy services

These helplines are starting up in many areas. Hopefully they will be well advertised so they will be used by those who need them most. The majority of them are likely to be funded by health authorities or Social Services departments and run by voluntary organisations, often, but not always, concerned with severe mental illness. The sort of help available will be as much influenced by the policy of those funding them as by the aims and objectives of those providing the service, but, as a minimum, there should be readily available information on local community services.

The new advocacy services that are also springing up nationwide are concerned with making sure that users (sufferers) understand their rights and that their wishes are heard and understood.

There has been less concern with the similar needs of carers and it may be that separate facilities will be made available for them. This would seem to be a pity as a combined service would quickly make it clear to service providers that the rights carers seek are, more often than not, those that guarantee a more effective service for sufferers, that is, care and protection for their relatives, particularly at those times when they are vulnerable and not aware of their need for this.

Accommodation

The choice of available accommodation becomes an important issue for those sufferers who do not have the option of living with their families, for whatever reason. Also, although many sufferers with an ongoing, persistent illness prefer to stay in the family home, a few reach the stage where they would like to live independently from the family, which would have happened if they had not had an illness. Finally, it may also become an issue for those individuals whose long-term carers have died or are becoming very elderly and frail as well as anxious to see their relative well settled in an alternative home before they die.

Moving home requires careful consideration anyway, but this is particularly the case for anyone having to cope with an ongoing serious mental illness. Let's take a look first at the sorts of accommodation that provide varying levels of support for their residents.

Twenty-four-hour care hostels
Many of the seriously ill who have been long-term in-patients in the old mental hospitals are being transferred to these hostels out in the community. Usually staffed by trained nurses, these labour-intensive resources are likely to be used specifically for these ex-hospital in-patients and, perhaps, for any new and disabled sufferers who need continuing care that is not otherwise available for them.

Other hostels
Increasingly, hostels tend to be provided by the voluntary and private sectors and, as well as differing in the level of supervision, comfort and care provided, they also vary according to the policies of the individual organisations. A few provide a structured programme, others less so, with some providing little more than shelter and food.

Policies of the various organizations that run these hostels can vary considerably and these depend on their attitudes to mental illness and whether or not there is any real acknowledgement or understanding of the potential needs of someone trying to cope with a psychotic illness. This can mean that the staff of one hostel will regard it as one of their duties to keep an eye on their residents and to check that they take their medication and that they see a doctor if they seem to be physically or mentally out of sorts, while the staff of another hostel would see this as intruding on the individual's rights to privacy and self-determination. In theory, then, such rights are more important than keeping well and clearly this could affect the quality of life of an individual with a serious mental illness.

You may therefore want to check out the overriding policy and attitude of any recommended hostel, together with its other features, such as opportunities to have a single bedroom and facilities for entertaining and chatting with visitors. Other features worth noting are whether or not real attempts are made to provide stimulating activities or to integrate residents into the local community or, at the other extreme, if they are allowed to stay in bed all day and do nothing if they wish. It does happen!

Unless you have ample private means, then obtaining a place in a hostel will depend on the result of an assessment by Social Services, as that department will be expected to allocate the funding for the placement. Nevertheless, there is likely to be an element of choice of hostel, depending on fees and the availability of places and funding.

Group homes

For several decades, group homes have proved to be a cheap and reasonably effective method of providing sheltered housing for the chronically ill (often former long-term in-patients) in the community.

Ideally, these resources provide separate bedrooms and a shared kitchen and lounge for around six or so residents, who benefit from the regular and ongoing support of a social worker or community psychiatric nurse, perhaps backed up by a group of volunteers who take an interest in the welfare of the residents.

If there is enough support from the system and the residents are compatible, then this can work quite well and may be worth considering by anyone who would rather be part of a small community than live apart from others.

Sheltered bedsit and flatlets

This sort of accommodation allows for more independent living than that provided by a group home, but without most of the risks inherent in 'going it alone' in unsupervised accommodation. At best, this will provide single living units within the same building for similarly vulnerable residents, together with a communal room and, perhaps, laundering fcilities. The added bonus of a motherly or fatherly figure for a few hours a day to keep an eye on things and perhaps cook an evening meal is a rare but invaluable extra provision!

Unfortunately there is litle of this sort of attractive and practical accommodation and, at the time of writing, there still seems to be no appreciation that many sufferers could manage very well if they lived in the sort of warden-controlled housing provided for the elderly.

During the 1980s, there was a brief move towards providing 'core and cluster' facilities for individuals with a serious mental illness. With these, a 'cluster' of bedsits, or similar accommodation, is provided near to a 'core' resource, such as a hostel or day centre. This can provide the best of both worlds – independent living with accessible help and support from a nearby staffed resource. These seem to be few and far between, but, if such an arrangement sounds attractive to you, it may be worth checking to see if there is any such scheme in your locality.

Financial considerations

There is one outstanding advantage with groups homes and sheltered bedsits and flatlets. Some sufferers find it very difficult to cope with all the usual household bills, particularly when money is in short supply anyway, and sheltered accommodation ensures that this administrative chore is kept to a minimum. Living in a group home or other sheltered accommodation involves the paying of one fee to cover all household bills, leaving the remainder of your money free for food, clothing and personal expenses.

Rather differently, living in a hostel involves the paying of one fee, deducted at source, to cover everything except for your personal needs. Sadly, though, the present system allows State-aided residents in the more expensive hostels such a tiny sum for themselves that those individuals who would most benefit from this type of care refuse it because they cannot even afford to support the smoking habit that so often accompanies an ongoing chronic mental illness.

Ordinary accommodation

As there is an acute shortage of suitable sheltered housing for vulnerable members of our society, too many sufferers settle for living in isolated bedsits in awesome high-rise flats or some other disadvantaged housing, in dingy unregistered lodgings or frequently in soul-destroying bed and breakfast accommodation.

None of these is likely to provide MD or schizophrenia sufferers with a reasonable amount of stimulation or with the feeling that they are part of a community. Indeed, this type of living accommodation encourages withdrawal from the rest of the human race and doing nothing all day long, thus reinforcing the worst effects of a schizophrenic or depressive illness. As a general rule, while most individuals with this type of illness need space and privacy, they also have a need to have other people around them. Pessimistic thoughts and paranoid ideas can thrive on loneliness. Take heed and persist in demanding something better than this for you and yours!

The perils of isolation

Without wishing to sound discouraging, it has been my experience that few sufferers do well living on their own and it has been saddening to hear seemingly well men and women expressing a deep reluctance to return to an empty flat, or whatever, after a few happy hours in the company of others. If you suspect that this is likely to apply to you, do consider very carefully any proposals that, while providing greater independence and privacy, may, nevertheless, leave you feeling isolated. The chances are that you have an even greater need to have people around you than the rest of us and this may be essential for your future wellbeing. Therefore, make sure that you talk about this with those you trust and take your time over such an important decision.

10

The law – its use and abuse

When we talk about a crisis in serious mental illness we are referring to a psychotic breakdown. It is the potential risks incurred by such a breakdown that has led to the word 'serious', and even 'severe', being used with this type of illness. But, what are these risks?

First of all, and most commonly, each breakdown can bring with it gradual, but real, deterioration and, at worst, can lead into an irreversible chronic illness. Also, untreated psychosis can lead to potentially disastrous events that can wreck one's social standing and lifestyle, important relationships and career plans. Even more tragically, untreated psychosis can can lead to a person 'slipping through the net' and landing up in prison or on the streets. At worst, it can lead to suicide or even homicide – we have all read newspaper headlines that highlight those few cases which lead to the death of others, and whether they be strangers or family, they are nearly always the victims of a psychotic paranoia.

Psychosis – a special dilemma

If we bear in mind that by the time they are becoming psychotic, MD and schizophrenia sufferers are quite sure that *they* are not mentally ill, then it is easier to understand why doctors and other professionals find it difficult to intervene and 'stop the rot'. In most other circumstances in which patients are temporarily unable to seek help for themselves, such as with delirium or diabetic coma, for example, then the next of kin, or anyone else for that matter, can ensure that help is obtained. Sadly, it is not so simple with a suspected psychotic illness as no one can force treatment for such a condition on someone without recourse to the law and this can involve a procedure that can be amazingly cumbersome.

Not only is it cumbersome, but there is a deep-seated reluctance among GPs and mental health professionals to use the law *before* a real crisis has blown. Although this is usually founded on humane considerations – a reluctance to take away someone's freedom and 'label' them seriously mentally ill – such professionals do not seem to appreciate that the law may be the only recourse once the sufferer has become psychotic. At this point, the only consideration should be the protection of the individual.

Timely prevention

More importantly, many professionals seem to be unaware of the vital factor we have mentioned several times in this book – the critical period *before* a psychosis strikes, a time when the individual will accept help. In nearly all cases, such help will be an adjustment or resumption of medication and a little moral support.

Just so there is no confusion at this stage, it may help sufferers and their families to compare this preventive approach – a prescription of a temporary, often small, increase in medication, with the individual's permission – with what happens if no action is taken before a full breakdown occurs. If no action is taken, after sometimes long delays and further deterioration leading up to a potentially dangerous crisis, what is then required is usually admission to hospital and the prescription of *enormous* amounts of the same medication just to break through the psychosis. If successful, this may well then be followed by a long haul back (a year or more is not unusual) to normality. Even then, there is no guarantee that the individual would regain the state of health enjoyed prior to the breakdown.

Because of this and because the system fails most sufferers at this critical period when they are still able to accept help, it is essential that the law should be used to stop the damaging process of a psychotic illness sooner rather than later. Before we consider this further, let's first look at the legal process called *sectioning*. It is all about getting someone into hospital and putting them on the medication they need when this is the only means by which their psychosis can be arrested.

The Mental Health Act 1983 – a resource

It is under this legislation that someone can be compulsorily admitted to hospital 'in the interests of his own health or safety or with a view to the protection of other persons.' We call this Sectioning and, with the appropriate medical support, a Section can be applied for by an approved social worker (ASW) or, more rarely, by the *nearest relative*, as defined by the law.

The nearest relative

This individual has important rights, particularly when it comes to getting help in a pending or actual crisis. The term does not necessarily equate with the next of kin as might be expected. The 'nearest relative' in law is determined by reference to a list that clarifies the order of priority for a sufferer's relatives, as follows:

- husband or wife
- son or daughter
- father or mother
- brother or sister
- grandparent
- grandchild
- uncle or aunt
- nephew or niece.

All these relatives need to be of adult age.

Where two relatives have equal priority, then the *elder* of the two, regardless of sex, will be the choice, with half-blood relationships taking second place.

In certain situations, the list becomes inappropriate. For example, if the patient normally resides with a relative, then that individual will be the nearest relative. Equally, if the patient has lived with a *non*-relative as husband or wife for at least six months prior to admission to hospital, then that person is considered to be the nearest relative. If the patient has lived with a non-relative, but *not* as husband or wife (as might be the case in a homosexual relationship, for instance), for five years, then that person is considered to be a 'relative', but not necessarily the *nearest* relative.

The nearest relative's role in a crisis

The nearest relative has two important rights that relate to getting help in a crisis. First, he or she may request that the local Social Services department provide an ASW to carry out a mental health assessment of the sufferer 'with a view to making an application for that individual's admission to hospital' (ie, to Section the individual) and if the ASW decides not to make an application, then that officer has to inform the 'nearest relative' in writing of the reasons for this. Second, the 'nearest relative' can opt to make the application at the time that an ASW declines to do so – or later – if there is medical support for a Section (ie, without waiting for the 'reasons in writing').

Importantly, the nearest relative is *not* the applicant of choice if an ASW *is* available and willing to do this as everyone agrees that this is a burdensome responsibility for someone who is likely to be emotionally involved with the sufferer. However, the nearest relative is certainly the *alternative* applicant. This right was hard fought for by organisations such as the National Schizophrenia Fellowship as they wanted to provide a safety net for sufferers on those occasions when the *family* knows that their relative is in desperate need of hospitalization and medical help and *doctors* are recommending it, but an ASW decides there is *no* need for this. And it happens!

I have met family members who have been unaware of this right when they needed to know about it *even though* ASWs have a duty to make this clear to them and this is stated in the 1993 Code of Practice (a special guide for professionals working with this legislation and a worthwile buy for families). Similarly, ASWs have a duty to provide the necessary paperwork and guidance to enable the nearest relative to carry out the Section. If you have trouble with any of this, contact a manager at the local Social Services department or a manager at the hospital where the sufferer is to be admitted. This is important as there is no way that the nearest relative can get on with making an application under the Mental Health Act *without* the right paperwork and without guidance from professionals who work with the legislation.

Sectioning

Sectioning is the name gven to the process of compulsorily admitting someone to a 'safe place', usually a hospital. So long as there has been no question of criminal action, then there are just three Sections that sufferers and their families are most likely to come across at a time of crisis.

Section 2

This lasts for a period of up to 28 days and is intended to be used for assessment or for assessment followed by medical treatment, as appropriate.

Section 3

This lasts for a period of up to six months and is intended be used for treatment when the individual is known to be suffering from a mental illness.

Section 3, then, is intended for the provision of treatment where the patient is already known to have a mental illness. The length of time of this section provides adequate time for a treatment programme that should ensure a proper recovery.

We will take a further look at Section 3 later in this chapter as ASWs can be exhorted in their training to take the 'least restrictive action' and this, sadly, can result in some of them avoiding the use of Section 3, even though this can be ended as soon as the sufferer is well enough. Interestingly, use of Section 3 brings with it a further important advantage. When it expires, or is discharged, Social Services departments and health authorities have a duty between them to provide ongoing care under section 117 of the Mental Health Act – an excellent reason for making sure that good practice is adhered to!

Section 4

This is an emergency option that lasts for up to 72 hours. Section 4 only requires the involvement of one doctor and an ASW or nearest relative. Professionals are expected to use this section only in an emergency – for example, where there is an immediate an acute risk of harm to the sufferer or others. Quite apart from being poor practice, the use of this section is not a good idea *except* in a very real emergency as, all too often, a sufferer may calm down after a few hours in hospital and apparently 'recover', only to be discharged with nothing at all having been resolved.

The right to appeal

There is one more important feature of the system that families need to know about.

One of the first things that happens when sufferers are admitted to hospital is that they are invited to appeal against this compulsory detention (in the case of a Section 2, within the first 14 days). Let's get this into perspective: when others eventually do take responsibility for protecting sufferers from their illness and arrange for them to be admitted to hospital, they are then invited to appeal against this action (perhaps confirming their conviction that the rest of the world has gone mad?) Many do appeal and tribunals are set up at great expense, in terms of lawyers' costs and health professionals' time, with sufferers occasionally being discharged from their section before their treatment is complete (remember, a Section 2 lasts only 28 days) and against the supervising doctor's wishes, sometimes with dire results. In the case of a Section 3, it is likely that a tribunal will not take place until around half-way through the permitted six-month period, but this again brings with it the risk of the individual being discharged before treatment has been completed.

Tribunals

These tribunals take place in an informal setting within the hospital caring for your relative. They are managed by a panel of three; a lawyer (chair), a doctor and lay person. The professionals who supervise the patient's care prepare reports that should include the family's viewpoint about what is happening, and each attends personally as required. The nearest relative (or a personal representative) may attend the tribunal and make a contribution, and other relatives or a friend, as appropriate.

Hospital managers should notify families about an impending tribunal, so do check for yourself that you will be kept informed about this matter, as it may be important for you to attend if you have remaining concerns about the health and welfare of your relative. Bear in mind that your relative may well be represented by a lawyer.

Make no mistake about it, in some cases, your participation may make all the difference to the panel's understanding of the extent of the sufferer's problems.

Why the mental health legislation is important

The above is a brief and simplified outline of the Mental Health Act, as it applies to the most commonly used sections and so I recommend once more that if you and your family are having to cope with a serious mental illness, you read the Code of Practice 1993 and keep it by you for future reference. It may well be, however, that it is even more important that you should have some idea of the politics surrounding the use of the mental health legislation.

A civil liberties issue?

Perhaps having had no option but to await the point of crisis in their relative's illness, many families are then amazed and alarmed to find that the emphasis suddenly focuses on *political* rather than *medical* matters – issues such as the right to be free and not detained in hospital and the right to refuse treatment and care.

This political influence dates back to the 1960s and the birth of the anti-psychiatry movement; the debate about such rights has raged from that time. The irony is that it has not concerned itself in the meantime with rights that seem more positive and more relevant, such as the right to be protected from tormenting fears, the right to be cared for and the right to be well.

This whole debate has had considerable influence on mental health legislation world-wide. Sadly, it has had more far-reaching effects on the attitudes of those working with serious mental illness and many who actually work with the mental health legislation in this country are very ambivalent about using it. Although this may not be acknowledged as such or even consciously recognised by all of these professionals, this reluctance shows itself in various widespread misconceptions that seem impervious to reason. Just three of these may be of interest to families trying to get help in a crisis.

1 A reason for not using the law?

Professionals explain their reluctance to use the mental health legislation by pointing out that being sectioned can ruin someone's life by, for example, spoiling their chances of getting a job, adopting a child, emigrating and so on.

Such a reply demonstrates how little they understand about society's present intolerance of *any* serious illness, let alone psychosis. Once sufferers have such a diagnosis on their medical file, then this, on its own, can affect their chances of getting a job and preclude any hopes of adopting a child or emigrating, as well as causing problems with obtaining insurance and a car licence and, perhaps, accommodation. Furthermore, whereas many potential employers take great care to ask questions about a candidate's medical history (even asking if they take medication), they do not ask about sectioning. Why should they? If one breakdown 30 years ago can spoil a candidate's chance of getting a job in some circumstances, what has sectioning to do with anything?

Not only can professionals working with the mental health legislation be ignorant about such rather obvious matters, but some compound this with another type of ignorance.

Meg

Meg is still perturbed about what happened to her daughter several years ago when she was recovering from a second schizophrenic breakdown. Sadly it had been necessary for Meg to do the section because the ASW had not taken seriously anything that she, or two doctors involved, had to say and declined to apply for a section. They in turn, correctly decided on a Section 3 as the young woman's illness had been diagnosed previously and was known to local professionals.

Meg's daughter made good progress and, five weeks or so later, she was becoming well again. However, Meg found her in tears and quite hostile when she visited one afternoon. She eventually learned that social workers had told the young woman that her mother had ruined her career, that she wouldn't be able to get work again because she had been sectioned, and particularly as this was a Section 3.

When professionals behave in this way, one suspects that they may be obsessed with civil liberties issues to the exclusion of all other humane considerations. It is certainly a case of putting ideologies before people, so far have some 'caring professionals' come from caring! Fortunately, Meg's daughter has resumed a successful career and she and her mother remain good friends. When completely recovered, her daughter judged her *mother's* type of caring to be the one that best served her interests and future welfare.

2 Using the law too late?

There is a widespread belief among mental health professionals and GPs that someone is not sectionable unless there is deemed to be a immediate likelihood of them harming themselves or others. This interpretation of the law is the main reason for the delays that put the sufferer, and possibly others, so much at risk. However, the law makes no requirement for the need to demonstrate that there is an immediate danger of sufferers harming themselves or others. Indeed, the Foreword of the Code of Practice 1993 points out:

> It has been widely reported that the criteria for admission to hospital under the Act have not been correctly understood by all professionals. In particular, there is said to have been a misconception that patients may only be admitted under the Act if there is a risk to their own or other people's safety. In fact the Act provides for admission in the interests of the patient's health, or of his or her safety, or for the protection of other people. This is clearly spelt out in the new paragraph 2.6 of the Code.

The fact that this very clear statement, together with various similar and widely circulated notices from the Department of Health over recent years, has seemingly brought about so little change in practice might suggest there is a will to avoid using the law or to delay taking any action until there can be no doubt whatever about the dire urgency for this. Certainly, it may be possible to maintain this viewpoint if one doesn't have to face the consequences of such delays. Unfortunately, suffers and those who love them do have to do this, but professionals frequently don't even receive feedback on how a psychotic crisis is eventually resolved. They are protected from having to face the results of their own decisions. This is a great pity as those responsible for good practice do not need such protection, while those whose practice is more questionable have little opportunity to learn or to have their work come under the sort of scrutiny that befits the considerable powers and responsibilities they are given.

Either way, while this situation remains and some families come to regard professionals as '*by-standers*' rather than helpers, then there is a strong case to be pro-active and to remember that there is every justification for insisting on help before things get desperate; 'in the interests of the patient's health'.

3 Using the law inappropriately?

As mentioned earlier, it may be helpful to bear in mind that ASWs in training may still be urged to 'take the least restrictive action' at all times and that this can result in relapsing sufferers being detained on a 28-day Section 2 instead of a 6-month Section 3, which, as we have noted, is intended for treatment for a sufferer whose illness has been previously diagnosed but that can, anyway, be discharged immediately the individual is well. The *law* has allowed for ample time for the successful treatment of a relapsing patient, but *professionals*, working with the legislation, may be encouraged to believe it is more humane to use the shorter Section. This can put sufferers at risk of recurring relapses because inadequate time has been given for them to make a proper recovery from the previous one.

Grant

I met Grant at a time when he was just getting over his second manic breakdown. The first episode of his illness had occurred when he was studying at university, and he made such a good recovery that doctors suspected he might now stay well. Indeed, when he was back at university a year or so later, it was agreed that he should come off his medication.

During the next vacation, Grant's mood was becoming high and no one was able to persuade him that this was happening. He eventually had to be admitted to hospital again, but he was put on a Section 2, although his illness had been recognised and treated previously.

During the first two weeks of the Section he was on anti-psychotic medication to 'bring down' his mania and he was reintroduced to his maintenance lithium treatment towards the end of the 28 days. He discharged himself immediately his 28-day Section ended and before the doctor wanted him to leave. However Grant seemed well enough, until someone mentioned his recent illness and then it quickly became clear that his 'recovery' was an illusion. He did not believe he had been ill – he believed he had been 'got at' by his family. This bright and potentially fit young man had not had long enough to get a proper grip on reality in hospital and it was no surprise to hear that, several weeks later, he was no longer taking his medication.

Early the next term, he returned home with the comment 'college is boring and the lecturers are idiots'. He didn't go back. His mother reported to his psychiatrist what had happened and that her son was edgy and not sleeping, but no one followed this up. Soon, Grant was admitted to hospital, again on a Section 2. He discharged himself immediately this Section was completed and before the doctors pronounced him well enough to go. He also announced his intention of moving out of the family home as he considered it his relatives' fault that he had been admitted to hospital again.

After this whole scenario had occurred a couple more times, Grant bore little resemblance to the young man he was two years earlier. His lack of insight, escalated by frequent breakdowns and admissions for treatment that were too brief, had ruined his chances of making a proper recovery and fulfilling a seemingly bright potential. His doctors *knew* he was not well enough for discharge each time, but did not feel they could justify detaining him further at that stage, and the various professionals who sectioned him each time chose to take 'the least restrictive action' and ignore the intention of the law and the guidelines in the Code of Practice. Neither Grant nor his now alienated family have benefited from this poor and misguided practice.

Summing up

First, as we have seen, professionals may regard the use of the law as prejudicing a sufferer's future, when this has anyway already been prejudiced by their illness.

Second, they may regard the use of the Mental Health Act as a last resort and not available for use unless sufferers can be seen to be a danger to themselves or others, although this is *not* actually a requirement of the law.

Third, even when there is no question about the *need* for a Section, then the law may be used to *minimum* affect. Thus, after all the trauma involved with a Section, the sufferer may still be given the shortest possible time for treatment and may well become permanently damaged in the process because inadequate time is allowed for the sufferer to become well again and achieve a proper grip on reality.

Another way forward?

There can be little doubt that there is one matter on which everyone is agreed (albeit for different reasons) that waiting for a crisis and having to use the law is not a desirable solution to the handling of serious mental illness. Nevertheless, until such time as everyone's energy focuses on the much better and *only* alternative – the recognition and skilled use of the critical period *before* a psychosis sets in – then the proper use of the law remains the only way that a sufferer can be protected from unnecessary suffering and damage. This help can only be made available if there is acknowledgement that the law allows for this preventive action in the interests of the patient's health.

Until the advent of self-management measures (such as those discussed in Chapter 4), which allow sufferers to adjust their medication as the need arises and to make advance directives requesting their admission to hospital to prevent a crisis, then families have no choice but to be proactive and press for good professional practice under the mental health legislation. I hope this chapter will help to make this easier for your family if the need arises. The next chapter will also focus on avoiding crisis situations.

11

Finding your way around the system

Let's assume your daughter is turning into a stranger in front of your eyes and all your attempts to do something about this have failed. She eventually agrees, rather reluctantly, to go and see the family's GP, but this has achieved little more than a sick certificate and advice to get some rest, which is all she has been doing for months anyway, as far as you can see. So, what do you do next?

Getting into the system

First, you need to make sure that your GP is made aware of what is really happening. As we saw in Chapter 9, it is this professional who can access the whole range of available mental health services. This is perhaps just as well as most of us have little idea about whom to turn to when someone close to us first becomes mentally ill. However, it is worth bearing in mind that GPs do not have specialist training in psychiatry and that they are also becoming increasingly busy with the pressures of today's National Health Service and usually have more than enough patients waiting to see them in their surgery. It is therefore a good idea to write down a list of the problems that are causing you concern for the doctor and to keep a dated copy of this list for your own records. You are thus making things as simple and straightforward as possible for your GP and, if there should be a later relapse, you will be able to refer back to your list, with 'Look, this is what happened the *first* time she was becoming ill'.

Medical confidentiality

It is possible that a GP may refuse to discuss your daughter with you on the grounds of 'medical confidentiality' if she is over 18 years of age. This makes life more difficult (and may not bode well for any hopes you may have of ongoing support from this doctor if your daughter's problems persist), but you can still hand in a letter at the surgery listing your concerns, and of course, keep a copy for your own records.

Explaining what is happening

Be as precise as you can in your list or letter. It is not easy to explain how someone has changed, but it's not really helpful to say, 'she seems strange' or 'she's become sulky and avoids the rest of the family all the

106

time'. Instead, think carefully and try to explain why this is worrying you so much.

If your daughter is an adolescenet, a difficult stage anyway, then a doctor might not be at all surprised that she is 'playing up' and doesn't want to bother with her family. However, is it just the family she is avoiding? Is she also avoiding her friends? Is she refusing to go to school or to work? Has she given up her hobbies and interests? Has she stopped watching television, even her beloved soaps, which she used to watch avidly? Does she instead sit in her bedroom for hours on end with the curtains drawn? Does she vanish the minute a visitor comes into the house? Does she even seem to be losing interest in her appearance and personal hygiene?

Importantly, some of these changes would *not* be characteristic of normal adolescent behaviour. For example, while teenagers often become stroppy with their parents and choose to spend their time with their friends (who also believe adults are stupid and don't understand), they certainly don't lose interest in their appearance and hygiene or avoid these same friends!

Similarly, does she refuse to eat with the family, but raid the bread bin and cake tins every time she gets the chance? Has her appetite changed? For example, has she previously always been careful about her diet but is now stuffing down loads of sweet, stodgy food? Has her sleep pattern changed? Is she up most of the night, say, and wanting to sleep during the day or, alternatively is she claiming she does not need sleep and certainly doesn't seem to be having much? Is she impatient with everyone and dismissive of their comments and opinions? Is she intent on making unrealistic plans or becoming increasingly reckless with her money and possessions, despite normally being organised and tending to be cautious? Is she having dramatic mood swings with unexplained highs and lows or is she wretched and miserable for no reason that those closest to her can determine? Are others in the immediate family worried about her in the same way that you are? How would they describe their concerns? All of these things could be important, but the emphasis should be on *what has changed* in your daughter and any deterioration you have seen since you first became concerned.

A stalemate situation

One of several things might happen at this stage. It is worth bearing in mind that your doctor's position is not an enviable one because as the young woman becomes more psychotic, so she is less likely to accept that she has an illness, let alone feel that she needs to see a doctor. She may well refuse to visit the surgery and some GPs take the stance that they cannot force their attentions on an unwilling patient by calling at their home. Similarly, your daughter may quite effectively deceive the doctor into thinking nothing is wrong. Remember, when sufferers feel threatened, they can behave quite normally for periods of up to an hour or so, only to fall apart immediately the threat has been removed and the professional is no longer present.

If, for whatever reason, your efforts to involve GP culminate in what may seem to you to be a stalemate situation, then keep the doctor informed of any deterioration, confirming this in writing and keeping a record for yourself. Do not hesitate to shout loudly if you feel that things are becoming desperate and, remember, you can request the GP to arrange for a psychiatrist to visit your home and assess your relative as this is a right available under the NHS and intended for just such a situation.

Involvement of the local mental health services

Some GPs will *not* have given up at this stage and may already be seeking the involvement of other professionals, either by requesting a home visit by a psychiatrist or by liaising with one of the local mental health teams.

Sooner or later, then, the GP or a psychiatrist may well involve other mental health professionals in your family's plight, probably requesting that a CPN or social worker call at your home and keep an eye on things. If this is the case, it might be a very good idea to stress the need, *immediately* this is mentioned, for the family to have access to this professional as well. All too often, the sufferer refuses to see the nurse or social worker and the family discover that that is that. A note is made in a file that your relative refused to see the professional and you are back where you started!

From the family's point of view, this can be a frustrating waste of a potentially good resource, who at the very least could offer ongoing advice and support and learn from *you* what is happening with your relative and with those trying to cope with the situation. Go for it – make your claim for help now in case, and before, this happens!

At a time of crisis

If things seem to be getting desperate and you don't know which way to turn, then one of the family (preferably the nearest relative – review the last chapter to remind yourself how to determine who this is) might ring the local Social Services department and ask for an ASW to come to the home and carry out a mental health assessment of your daughter. You might like to refer back to the last chapter anyway at this stage to remind yourself of what the sectioning process involves and what you need to be aware of *before*, rather than after, the event.

A *cautionary note*

It is worth noting that during 'out of hours' times, you may need to ring the local police station to find out how to contact the Social Services department. This accomplished, explain to the duty ASW why you feel the matter is urgent.

You may find, like several families I know, that if you stress urgency and if you mention any previous examples or fears of violence, you will then be told to get in touch with the police. If this happens to you – if you are told at any time by professionals you are trying to involve in your crisis to 'call the police' or 'get in touch with the police if she becomes violent (again)' – then beware! Make it very clear to them that you are seeking the help of professionals who are trained to work with a severe mental illness and who have the benefit of an *appropriate* legal system with which to protect sufferers, and then confirm this in writing. Make no mistake about it, if they see a potential need to call the police, then there is clearly a need for ASWs and doctors to be using the mental health legislation.

There is a very fine line between the *mental health* and *criminal* systems and – not surprisingly – few families share the view that it is kinder to let their relative end up in prison rather than face the perceived stigma of being admitted to hospital for treatment and care for a severe mental illness.

A mental health assessment

As this is the process that has to be undertaken before the law can be used to resolve a psychotic crisis, then it may help you to be aware of what is likely to happen when professionals come to your home to assess your daughter.

You can expect at least three professionals to call at the house – an ASW and a psychiatrist and another doctor, preferably the GP. They may come at different times and it may be a long drawn-out process if the social worker has trouble arranging for all three to be available at the same time. You may also expect that at least one of these professionals – the ASW – will be assessing the domestic situation and members of the family as well as your daughter.

Depending on the skills and awareness of these practitioners, everything may turn out to be straightforward and simple, with your daughter being assessed and sectioned with a minimum of trauma for her and the rest of the family, and let's hope this will be the case.

However, pause for a moment and consider the following scenario.

One way of looking at things

If your daughter is like most sufferers I know, then you may well be in for a shock. You may find that, after hours or even days of chaos within your home, suddenly she will be transformed. She will seemingly be in charge of the situation, perhaps meeting visiting professionals at the door and offering to make tea for them (yes, really!) In stark contrast, you and the rest of the family are likely to be suffering from nervous exhaustion and your daughter's riveting performance should guarantee that you are stunned and virtually incoherent!

Now, can you picture the scene which so very often greets the visiting professional? We have a fluent and welcoming individual whom other members of the family are claiming is really quite mad, together with one or more relatives who appear to much better fit such a description. The newcomer sees no evidence of the terror that is causing the adrenalin to course through your daughter's veins and enable her to give the performance of a lifetime, but becomes *very* aware of the agitation and near hysteria of her exhausted and now quite desperate family.

The chances are that you will be anxious to explain why you believe your daughter urgently needs help and you are likely to only feel able to do this privately rather than risk upsetting her any more than she has been before the professionals arrived. However, the ASW is duty-bound under the law to 'suitably' interview the sufferer, that is, in an unrushed and private setting if at all possible. There is no such obligation to provide the same facility for you (even if you are the 'nearest relative'), although the Code of Practice makes it clear that as much information as possible should be obtained from relatives and any others who may be involved.

Those professionals who believe in psychotic illness and appreciate the falseness of the situation they are likely to find on entering the home will make sure you have an opportunity to properly explain the events that have led up to your request for help. They will probably use what you tell them to ask your daughter the sorts of questions that can break through her temporary defence and enable them to verify the abnormality of her recent behaviour.

Another way of looking at things

Other professionals may do none of these things, but, instead, will accept the scenario at face value when they arrive. As you will have gathered, your daughter believes *she* is not ill, but that her *family* has become hostile and threatening, even quite mad. To your amazement you may find that 'the experts' carrying out the mental health assessment agree with her! You may find that they accept your daughter's version of what is happening rather than yours. Unfortunately, they may have been led to believe that they hear two different versions of what's been happening because of existing conflict in the home rather than because one party is probably psychotic and out of touch with reality. For example, when talking about mental health assessments, some ASWs talk of 'trying not to take sides' too quickly, that is, they see their role as having to decide *who* is at fault for what is happening, not *what* is at fault. If they, and sometimes other professionals too, are very much influenced by training that has evolved from the old family theories discussed earlier, then they may have a deep commitment to defend the sufferer from being scapegoated and labelled, as they see it.

It is not too hard to appreciate that what they see in your home may merely confirm such strange ideas. Even while your daughter is giving a (terrorised) performance of a lifetime, you are now beginning to realise that the impossible may be happening. Having reluctantly waited for the promised 'crisis', you are now beginning to suspect that still no one is going to do anything to resolve this nightmare. You may well feel that you or everyone else is going mad, and it probably shows! You may also shortly find yourselves back in the same situation – but worsened by the ordeal your daughter has just been through – with the professionals having departed. This can and does happen, and you then have to start the process of trying to get help all over again.

Do, however, remember that if the two doctors are recommending that your daughter be admitted to hospital, then the 'Nearest Relative' can make the application instead of the ASW (see Chapter 10 for details and guidance).

Collusion in a psychotic delusion

Sometimes, this evasion or denial of a medical explanation for what is happening can lead to the professionals colluding in the sufferer's madness, albeit possibly unwittingly.

Jane
Jane and her family know just how extreme this can be. She had kept well and lived a normal life for the nine years following her one acute schizophrenic episode with the help of a low maintenance dose of neuroleptic medication. With the agreement and encouragement of a doctor, Jane eventually weaned herself off this and, six weeks later, she was ill and 'on the run', rushing from one place to another and

causing great anxiety among friends and relatives along the way. Because of the concern of some of these, no less than 19 professionals became involved in 3 different counties over the next two months.

In all, dozens of hours were spent on this case without any one professional once seriously listening to Jane's parents' account of their daughter's previous breakdown and how she had kept well on a maintenance dose of medication ever since. Jane was much more fluent and coherent with each of the professionals in turn than her parents, who were exhausted with the worry and effort of trying to keep track of her whereabouts, realising how ill and vulnerable she had become. Each time they caught up with her, they had to try and persuade a different set of professionals that their daughter desperately needed help.

To their amazement, they were told that Jane was running away because of the way they treated her on a day-to-day basis (although she didn't live with them). This assumption was based on the increasingly bizarre and incredible statements she was making along the way. The 'experts' were believing these rather than her parents' own simple statements, and back-up evidence, of a previous, acknowledged, psychotic illness. Worse, even as the family begged for help for the young woman, so it dawned on them that no one was actually providing any practical help or doing anything about Jane's chaotic lifestyle – they were just spending hours listening to her fluent and increasingly bizarre monologue, choosing to believe this and then leaving her to get on with it.

Eventually, Jane's illness became too severe for this to be ignored any longer and she had to be admitted to hospital for treatment and protection. Her agitated depression disappeared within days of resuming medication and her delusions faded in the following weeks. She and her family discovered later that her delusions, together with the predictably inaccurate assumptions of professionals who had believed them, had been recorded in her files as factual. Furthermore, at one stage, one of her statements had been reported to the local police and actually acted upon!

When Jane recovered, she wanted to know how professionals trained to work with psychotic illness could have come to believe her delusional ideas? She was not the first to ask this. As one young man whose family had a similar experience has put it, 'Well, I know why I believed those mad ideas of mine, but what was *their* excuse?'

Hopefully, your family will not have an experience like this, but it may help to be aware that such things can happen. If you find yourself in a similar situation, then it may be a very good idea to speak immediately with someone in senior management and demand that service providers concern themselves with the facts of the case, that is, with the individual's past history and any changes that have taken place recently. At least then you will know that you have done everything you can to put the truth before the people who are meant to be helping you!

The police – the last resort?

When mental health professionals seemingly turn their backs on a crisis, it is quite often the police who eventually intervene and resolve this. The police have unwittingly become the resource of last resort and have earned the grateful respect of many families waiting in vain for help from the mental health services. This fact has been well recorded in carers' surveys during the past ten years or so.

However, whereas Section 136 of the Mental Health Act 1973 allows the police to arrest someone who is making a nuisance of themselves in a public place, seemingly because they are mentally ill, in order that they can then take the individual to a 'safe place' for assessment by mental health professionals, it becomes more difficult to keep a sufferer in the mental health system who is running riot within the home. Because of this, too many sufferers are finding their way into the criminal system simply because of the delays that take place in obtaining effective help from the mental health services. This tragic irony seems to have escaped those health professionals who hesitate to use the mental legislation. While they stand back and wait, sufferers run a real risk of falling foul of criminal law instead!

However, sometimes there seems to be no alternative but to seek urgent help from the police. If this happens to you, then make sure that everyone is aware that you have been in touch with the mental health services, quoting names of professionals who have been involved, and emphasise that your relative is mentally ill and needing medical treatment.

A crisis resolved!

Don't be discouraged by these cautionary tales of how things can go wrong for some families. It is better to be forewarned of potential pitfalls in the system than to have to rely on hindsight. The more aware you are, the more likely it is that you can make the system work for you and yours.

Now let's assume that your family's crisis has been resolved and that your daughter is now safely in hospital awaiting assessment and appropriate treatment.

113

Proper treatment and care

Hopefully your family will now have a chance to switch off and slow down for a few days now that your concerns have been acknowledged and your relative has been admitted to hospital. If this is a first-time episode of psychosis, then it should not be long before this is quickly recognised, diagnosed and treated with one of the appropriate drugs. If so, there is every likelihood that the sufferer will calm down and feel more relaxed quite quickly and, within a few weeks, most of the bizarre symptoms will be fading as well. If this doesn't happen, then the supervising psychiatrist will probably increase the medication or prescribe a different, but similar, drug.

Sharing, or otherwise, of a diagnosis

You will hope that the doctor will share the diagnosis with the family, and, when the time is right, with the sufferer. It is well worth seeking explanations if they are not forthcoming as some doctors are very squeamish about sharing a diagnosis of MD or schizophrenia and sufferers and families can be left high and dry without any of the information they need to find a way forward.

Fortunately, most doctors will appreciate the need for explanations and some may suggest that another professional on the staff team should spend some time with relatives so that they can ask at least some of the questions they need answered. Ideally, both the sufferer's progress and the information that doctors will share with you should enable you to cope with your natural anxiety at this time. You can help here by being patient and appreciating that recovery may be slow and painstaking and that your relative will thrive – as we all do – on reassurance and encouragement.

A second opinion

If you find you are unable to get any sensible explanations or if you have concerns that the psychiatrist supervising your relative's treatment appears to have doubts as to what that treatment should be, or worse, to have doubts about psychosis being a treatable condition, then you may come to feel that you want to seek a second opinion. This is your right, either under the NHS or on a paying basis. Similarly, if a sufferer has a new doctor who is not offering the treatment that has always worked in the past for your relative or if doctors are suddenly using the term 'personality disorder' about someone who has previously been treated successfully for a psychotic *illness* (we touched on this subject briefly in Chapter 1), then it may be a good idea to seek a second opinion. It may then also be worth seeking advice from the National Schizophrenia

Fellowship's Advice Line (see the Useful addresses section at the back of the book for the number) about psychiatrists who believe psychosis is a disease that can be treated and who are dedicated to finding ways to make life easier for the seriously mental ill and their families.

Discharge and aftercare

Once your relative has been stabilised on appropriate medication, the priority will be to ensure that discharge from hospital will not be a rushed or unplanned affair. It is worth noting that the Care Programme Approach (CPA) has been evolved to ensure that everyone leaving a psychiatric hospital has a formal discharge plan and that people being treated in the community will also have a programme of care. The team drawing up this programme may include the psychiatrist, nurses, your GP and social workers and should involve the patient and the family (provided the patient agrees, which should not normally be a problem *so long as any residual paranoid ideas have been recognised and resolved*).

The care package may include any of the services available under community care, as well as psychiatric treatment. As well as assessing the patient's health and social care needs, the CPA provides for a keyworker whose role is to maintain contact, ensure that the necessary services are provided and that the care package is regularly reviewed.

It may be worth bearing in mind that the Department of Health's Circular on the CPA emphasises that relatives and other carers (not always included in the making of discharge plans in the past, believe it or not) often know a great deal about the patient's earlier life, previous interests, abilities and contacts, and may have personal experience of the course of his/her illness spanning many years. Also that the patient or person being assessed should always be involved in discussions and should agree the programme to be implemented. In other words, there is a growing emphasis on involving sufferers and their families in forward planning in a way that has not been the norm in the past. You would be well advised to take advantage of this and to bear in mind ways in which your family and involved professionals might co-operate to protect your relative from future breakdowns.

Avoiding future relapse

Anyone who has had to live through a psychotic crisis will know only too well that they have much to gain by avoiding a repeat of the experience. Add to this the mounting evidence that each relapse can inflict further, sometimes irreversible damage on the sufferer and there is a good case for avoiding more of the same.

Long experience has taught me that the best chance of achieving this is to put in place the following three-point plan.

1 Bearing in mind what helps and what doesn't

On a general level, this includes noting the sort of precautions described in Chapters 3 and 4, and, in particular, taking a self-management approach to becoming acquainted with the more specific factors that seem to help your particular relative.

2 Recognising the first and early signs of relapse

Again, some general risk factors apply, such as reducing or discontinuing medication, loss of more than one night's sleep in MD and unexplained hostility and withdrawal behaviour in schizophrenia.

More importantly, and again using a self-management approach, there should be recognition that there is a pattern of symptoms and signs of relapse that is particular to each individual sufferer. These signs can be noted from the start of an illness, with a careful record being kept of what happens at the time of a first episode of severe mental illness, as suggested earlier in this chapter.

There is a likelihood that *similar* early signs will be apparent if your relative becomes vulnerable again. Thus, the more the sufferer and the family are aware of these, the better the chance that one or both will recognise the risks early enough for the individual to accept help. It would therefore be useful for these signs to be noted by everyone concerned when the sufferer's care package is being drawn up.

3 Obtaining a prompt response from professionals

In all probability, this response will need to be an adjustment or resumpton of medication and this will require immediate sanction from the supervising psychiatrist, perhaps following an assessment by a CPN.

Ask at the time of the drawing up of the sufferer's care package if an immediate response can be guaranteed. If it is agreed that there is a likelihood that there may be delays (and these are legend) in reaching the psychiatrist in an emergency, perhaps it could be agreed that the GP will provide the appropriate prescription in such circumstances. In addition, consideration could be given to the sort of agreement being proposed by the Manic Depression Fellowship and described earlier that allows sufferers to adjust their medication as appropriate.

Summing up

These, then, are the sorts of measures you can take to try to ensure that your relative is never again subjected to a serious mental health crisis. The last chapter and this one have stressed some very good reasons for this being the goal of every sufferer and family. Good luck with your efforts to keep the psychosis at bay!

12

Meeting other practical needs

Once a diagnosis and appropriate treatment have been obtained, then it should be possible to start on the road to recovery and eventually decide when the time is right to start preparing for a gradual resumption of a normal daily routine.

Timing one's return to work

It may be that you have a job to return to and, if so, that is great. It is nevertheless important to take things slowly and cautiously and probably start work again on a part-time basis initially. It does seem that some sufferers find they are rushed into working again before they are ready. I have heard the same story again and again from individuals whose first attempt to return to work failed because they were persuaded to go back too soon.

Maybe doctors and employers sometimes underestimate the stresses on any one sufferer for a considerable period following a breakdown, particularly if they only have the chance to meet with and see the individual in an interview situation. It has been my experience that when sufferers are reluctant to return to work, it is usually because they instinctively know that they are not yet ready for this. It might be that they worry about coping with colleagues at work because they still have shadowy feelings of paranoia and feel that they might escalate under pressure or are aware that they still can't concentrate on anything for a reasonable length of time.

If this is the case with you, then it may well be that you should trust your own instincts and talk with family or friends about this, seeking their support if you feel you need it before speaking with doctors or employers. If this is not possible, then, hopefully, there is a professional you can approach and talk with informally so that you can carefully explain your fears and exactly how you are feeling.

Rather differently, if you have had a manic illness, then it may be that you are keen to rush back to work rather sooner than would be wise? It is worth bearing in mind that if you find you tend to be overconfident about most things at the present time – or if others feel this is the case – then restraint may be a good idea when it comes to returning to work. Have you tested your concentration levels? Have you tested your staying powers? How patient are you with others at this time? How realistic are you about your achievements? Do think about this as the last thing you need at this stage is a premature return to work, which can lead to a damaging failure situation.

Not having a job to return to

If you are able to eventually make a successful return to work, then this should be a real help and a positive path back to a normal life – one most sufferers would choose if their health, and the economy, allowed for this. However, those who don't already have a job when they fall ill (and this will be more common with schizophrenia because of the age of so many first-time sufferers) often find that the stigma of severe mental illness can be a real barrier to getting a job.

Few emloyers are informed and tolerant about mental illness and many employ doctors to protect their pension schemes. Joanne's case illustrates this exactly.

Joanne
Joanne recovered completely from an acute schizophrenic episode and went on to obtain an honours degree after studying at college, away from home, for three years.

She wanted to be a general nurse and was accepted for training by nine different hospitals in turn, pending a medical. At this stage in each application, she was turned down, despite having made excellent progress since her breakdown and a very positive reference from the psychiatrist who had supervised her treatment.

Joanne eventually earned the right to train after working for two years as an assistant nurse in a hospital in her home town, where she was already known through voluntary work she had done in the past. She went on to have a successful career.

Another client of mine was offered employment by one hospital, so long as she had come off her medication by the time she started her training! I am glad to relate that she decided to come down on the side of sanity and turned down this breathtakingly irresponsible offer, despite the fact that she had wanted the job for a very long time.

Both these young women have, eventually, done very well for themselves despite the markedly discriminatory attitude of a succession of doctors – of all people – employed by NHS institutions.

Discrimination

Sadly, if sufferers answer truthfully the questions about their medical history now included on so many application forms, they usually find that, regardless of aptitude, experience and qualifications, they don't get invited to an interview. They are considered too much of a financial risk.

This practice is not only unmerited, it reveals the sort of prejudice no longer tolerated in other areas – gender, race, religion or sexual preference. It also means that while most criminal convictions can be disregarded after five years have elapsed, an episode of psychotic illness cannot.

Such discrimination encourages some very able sufferers to be less than honest when they fill in applications for work. However, think carefully about this. Not only can it put you under intolerable pressure – even fearing taking a few days off sick in case of being 'found out' – falsifying information in this way can of course result in instant dismissal. This is all very unfair for individuals who already have more than enough stresses to contend with. So if you find yourself in this Catch 22 situation, what can you do about it?

Other ways of getting work

It may be easier to get into jobs that are not pensionable because they do not always require one to complete an application form and employers may be more interested in how the candidate interviews than in their past.

Similarly, I have sometimes advised sufferers to take temporary work because many employers frequently offer permanent jobs to temps who have proved they can do the work and who seem to fit in well.

Voluntary work

You might like to consider taking up voluntary work – in the short-term anyway. This can be rewarding and therapeutic. It can also sometimes lead to eventually achieving gainful employment by building up a record of work over a reasonable period *following* recovery from a serious mental illness, while hopefully obtaining encouraging references from those providing this work. It may also lead to opportunities to meet with and impress all sorts of people who may be able to help you when the time is right to look for work on the open market.

Voluntary work can also be an end in itself for sufferers who are unlikely to be well enough to hold down a normal job. Some find they can obtain quite challenging or specialist work that would not otherwise be available for them or would be too exacting in an ordinary work situation. This can be very rewarding as well as a boost to one's confidence.

Some individuals take up voluntary work over a short period just to help them get back into a routine as a preparation for returning to paid employment. Others become involved in the day-to-day running of, for example, the drop in centre they have been frequenting since becoming ill. Also, as we noted in Chapter 9, some of these centres are run on a 'Clubhouse model' and so may be able to help you prepare for and eventually find gainful employment.

Another obstacle

Before leaving the subject of voluntary work, a warning. Despite a very real lack of job opportunities during the first half of the 1990s, the Government has chosen this time to impose conditions on some benefits claimants, and these include limiting the number of hours allowed for studying or voluntary work. Because of this, it would be a good idea for claimants to first obtain general information on what the current situation is. This should be available in the form of leaflets and via free and anonymous helplines, both provided by the Department of Social Security (DSS) and listed under their entry in the phone book.

Sheltered workshops and industrial therapy units (ITUs)

These sorts of resources may have something to offer those sufferers whose ability to work has been seriously affected by their illness.

Sheltered workshops have an impressive history of providing training and work for the physically disabled as well as those having to cope with other disabilities and they can help to provide rehabilitation before entering paid employment as well.

ITUs were a popular type of mental health resource in the 1970s and 1980s, but many have disappeared with the closing of the hospitals to which they are attached. This is rather a pity as, at their best, they can provide a therapeutic and structured work situation for individuals who have a chronic illness, some of whom very much appreciate 'having a job' to go to each day in congenial surroundings.

These resources have been criticized for exploiting disabled sufferers by paying for most of their 'contract work' with pitifully low wages. Valid though this may be, such a viewpoint does overlook the fact that the pay of many sufferers is limited because of the restrictions on benefits claimants. It also misses the point that some individuals *choose* to spend their day in such a setting, particularly when an ITU is run by someone with a real understanding of their particular needs.

Studying

If you first became ill when away at college studying for a degree or vocational qualification, you will probably have gathered that this is very common. Many of those involved never complete their studies, but a few do.

In my experience, those who succeed are the same individuals who take it very slowly and first gradually wean themselves back to studying with a short period of reading each day and, when they feel ready, embark on a part-time course for a year or so – perhaps taking up something practical like a typing or computer course – gradually increasing the amount of study they do until they have proved to themselves that they can apply themselves to the work, that their ability to concentrate has returned.

Often sufferers yearn to get back to their studies and their former lifestyle, overlooking the fact that their powers of concentration and their ability to mix with and work with others may be impaired enough to make a premature return to college a disaster. Failure at this stage is very sad and all too common. My advice would be to go for it by all means, but to be realistic about this and not squander a precious opportunity. Take it slowly and first prove to yourself and everyone else that you've prepared yourself for taking up this second chance. Even then it won't be easy, but it can be done.

Not everyone will be involved or interested in higher education, but some sufferers will find it rewarding to become involved in other part-time education while they have time on their hands. This is becoming increasingly available at special rates for the unemployed and covers a considerable range of activities, from taking up a new hobby through to studying something that might be useful in the future.

However, a cautionary note for those on benefits. As mentioned above, there are restrictions on the number of hours of voluntary work claimants may do and this also applies for people wanting to study. So, obtain some informatiaon on how you stand *before* signing up for any courses.

Claiming State benefits

Many sufferers need to claim State benefits at one time or another. Some, who are unlikely to be well enough to hold down a job, have to rely on them indefinitely.

For several reasons – and these may become clear in the following paragraphs – it is important to establish with the DSS as soon as possible that you are suffering from an illness. If there have been delays in getting your diagnosis and finally establishing this *is* sickness, then seek medical support for getting your records backdated appropriately. Either way, it will be necessary to regularly submit 'sick' certificates once the benefit is being claimed. This will apply whether or not the benefit is means-tested or non means-tested. The advantage of the latter type of benefit is that it is unaffected by any other monies you may have now or any windfalls that might come your way in the future.

Non-means-tested benefits

Incapacity Benefit

This replaced Invalidity Benefit.

This benefit is reliant on the claimant having made enough National Insurance contributions over a recent and relevant 12 month working period. It is important to claim this benefit immediately you are unable to work. If you have been working regularly over a period of 12 to 18 months – and you establish that you are sick without undue delays once you are unable to work – then you should be entitled to this benefit.

Although the rules are now tighter than they were with the old Invalidity Benefit, if you have made the contributions and your doctor is prepared to confirm that you have a severe mental illness such as MD or schizophrenia, then this should entitle you to claim Incapacity Benefit.

There is a 'therapeutic earnings' rule attached to this benefit and it means that claimants may be able to do a few hours paid work a week once they are well enough to do this as well as claim benefit. They can do this so long as they have their doctor's backing and they adhere to the quite complicated DSS guidelines, which include having the permission beforehand of the local department's adjudicating officer to do the work.

Severe Disablement Allowance

Usually, the claimant has to prove an 80 per cent disability before this is payable. This can be achieved when a chronic sufferer is clearly going to be permanently unfit for any kind of work. However, it is unlikely to apply to most sufferers as they may be fit enough to work at least intermittently.

However – and this is important – anyone who has been incapable of work for a 6-month period and who is between 16 and 20 years of age can qualify for this benefit, as can older individuals who can prove that they have been unfit to work on a continuing basis since before their twentieth birthday.

This benefit pays less than Income Support (see below under means-tested benefits for further details), but, importantly, it can be topped up by this means-tested benefit, leaving the Severe Disablement Allowance component of your claim untouched by any windfalls that you might have at a later date.

The 'therapeutic earnings' rule (see under Incapacity Benefit above) also applies to this benefit

Disability Living Allowance

This has replaced the old Attendance Allowance (although it still applies to those over 65) and Mobility Allowance.

There are various bands of payment with both a 'care' and a 'mobility' element. The rules are complicated, but many individuals with schizophrenia and some with MD should qualify for the lower or middle bands under the 'care' element for any, or all, of the following reasons, so long as a mental health worker refers to their condition as a 'severe mental illness' (the official phrase for a psychotic illness):

- not being able to organize and prepare the main meal of the day for oneself
- needing to be reminded and monitored by others when it comes to taking one's prescribed medication
- needing to have someone to keep an eye on one each day.

It will be simpler soon to apply for this benefit when canges to the claim form will allow for 20 questions directly related to mental illness.

It should be noted that those who are awarded DLA who are also in receipt of Income Support (see below) and live independently (although residing in group home is acceptable) should qualify for an extra and worthwhile benefit called Severe Disability Pension (SDP). Do go ahead and claim SDP as, at the time of writing, it seems that there has been a wholesale failure to pay out this benefit automatically to those who qualify for it!

Please note that Disability Living Allowance should be claimed (via the appropriate application forms and with the backing of your doctor or a mental health professional who is involved with you) if you have been ill for three months and there is quite a reasonable chance of your remaining so for at least as long again.

Disability Working Allowance

This benefit was brought in during the early 1990s at about the same time as the Disability Living Allowance (see above), but I have yet to hear one good report about it!

It is aimed at disabled individuals who work for more than 16 hours per week. There seem to be all sorts of complications and delays over payments, which is the last thing that sufferers need. More importantly, there is a major problem in that it can jeopardize payment of Housing Benefit and this could be particularly disastrous in view of new rulings about the payment of claimants' rent. You might also like to refer to further comments about sufferers and intermittent work towards the end of this review of benefits.

Means-tested benefits

Income Support

This is now the mainstay of many sufferers' income, particularly those with schizophrenia, as the young age of onset of the illness can mean that they never qualify, number of contributions wise, for Incapacity Benefit.

Because Income Support is a means-tested benefit, it will not be payable if the sufferer has more than a certain amount of capital, so do check what the current rules are regardinging the allowable amount.

Once agin, sufferers who draw Income Support and who are unable to work because of their illness should regularly (from the word go, if possible) submit medical certificates to the DSS and, after six months, they will be entitled to a disability premium, which should boost their benefit by nearly half as much again and allow a small 'earnings disregard' as well.

It is important to realise that Income Support can be claimed as a 'top-up' to other benefits, such as Severe Disablement Allowance and Disability Living Allowance (see above under non-means-tested benefits). This is very worth while as Income Support brings with it a package of other privileges, such as help with NHS prescriptions, dental treatment, spectacles and fares for hospital treatment. It also entitles claimants to maximum Housing Benefit, which, at the time of writing, can amount to 100 per cent of one's rent and 80 per cent of Council Tax.

Social Fund

This replaced the old Single Payments system, which covered claims for the replacement of essential items and for emergencies. It comprises two schemes:

- *Community Care Grants*, which are intended for helping disabled people lead independent lives in the community and represent one-off payments to sufferers leaving hospital, or a similar institution, to help them settle down in the community.

- *Budgeting Loans*, which are interest-free loans to cover certain items of furniture and domestic expenses. Repayments for these loans will be deducted from your existing benefits, so the DSS will first check that you can afford these payments. They are, anyway, discretionary and will also depend on the take-up of this resource locally at any one time.

Comment

As may be apparent from the above, the benefits system is complicated and it sometimes seems to be all about endlessly filling in forms. Getting into *this* system can prove a frustrating and long-winded affair, but things may go quite smoothly once this is achieved.

Unhappily, the same problems tend to crop up each time claimants change their 'status', as for example, when being discharged from hospital or changing accommodation. On top of this, rather than reaping their just rewards, sufferers run real risks of losing benefits if they take a job and then find they are unable to persevere with this or get the sack – either of which is quite possible if they find working too stressful. It is not surprising, therefore, that those who have little chance of working permanently tend to be advised not to try, rather than subject themselves to these sorts of hazards while there is so little appreciation of the damage such stresses can cause them. It is therefore well worth thinking very carefully about this until such time as the system provides real encouragement for those who attempt to work, albeit it may be only temporary, rather than a series of punitive obstacles if and when they fail.

Payments by proxy

Importantly, the rest of your family or a friend might like to note that if you are too unwell to claim and draw benefits or if you refuse to do this – for whatever reason – then your local DSS office will be happy to explain how a third person can become an appointee for the claimant and, perhaps, save everyone extra and unnecessary financial worries.

Keep yourself informed

It is worth bearing in mind that the benefits system tends to change from time to time and this has been increasingly the case during the first half of the 1990s, so do double-check any of the above information if it is likely to affect your own situation.

Part IV   A mutually supportive network

13

Recognizing and dealing with uncomfortable emotions

For most families, there comes a time when they realise that there *is* life after serious mental illness and everyone gradually and individually adjusts to what has happened. The depth of this adjustment will depend, of course, on the persistence and extent of the sufferer's illness and on each family member's own personality and coping mechanisms. For example, how does one cope with uncomfortable emotions that may be around long after the first shock of a psychotic illness? Let's take a look at some typical examples:

Why me?

Perhaps the most common reaction to any damage wreaked by a serious mental illness is a sense of having been let down, having been allowed to assume that one's quite normal expectations would be fulfilled. We touched on what such disappointments and frustrations can mean for a sufferer in Chapter 5. At worst, it can amount to a sense of having lost oneself: at best, it begs the anguished question 'Why me?' This is a question often asked by other members of the family, too – 'Why has my Dad changed, why has this happened to *me*? and 'Why *our* marriage, why did my wife have to lose her vitality and love of life? Why has this happened to *me*?'

This is a very natural reaction and if you are the relative of a sufferer, though, you will know that they can lead to feelings of guilt and shame and having to remind yourself that you are not the real victim of this tragedy. But you are also a victim and, as such, you may need to rant and rave sometimes about what has happened. It is healthy, when the need arises, to put yourself first, to acknowledge your anger and frustration. It may even help you to soldier on until things improve rather than giving up or succumbing to poor health, which can help no one.

Why my *Child?*

In those sad cases where a sufferer has been badly damaged, it is not just the here and now that can be so frustrating, it is the *contrast* between now and what might have been. Never is this more apparent than in the parents of young people struck down at an age when they were just starting to fulfil their dreams and plans. How do these parents cope with knowing what their children have lost? How do they cope when they watch other young people go on to achieve what they wanted and what was expected of them? If this has happened to you, then you may have experienced pangs of envy quite foreign to your nature, alongside the pangs of guilt that accompany such natural feelings.

A special dilemma

You may also know that this pain has a special significance if it is associated with comparing your sick child's future with that of the rest of the family's – the anguish of finding it difficult to enjoy the usually prized successes of your other children because of what has happened to their brother or sister. Some parents are told when their child becomes seriously ill that they are lucky that they have other healthy children. Such a comment reveals a worrying lack of understanding of what it is like to be a parent.

Ellen and Tony

Ellen and Tony speak of the time their elder daughter was admitted to hospital and they were told by a doctor, 'you'll have to concentrate on your other children now'. They were appalled. At that time all their thoughts and attentions were centred on their sick child and it seemed that they were being encouraged to give up on her, to turn away and enjoy their other offspring.

Fortunately, most parents do not forsake the child who most needs them and Ellen and Tony were no exception. Their daughter eventually made a good recovery, but they found that while she was ill they tended to almost resent the normally sought-for successes of her younger brother and sister.

Joy

Joy is a wonderfully warm mother with a large family, each member of which she adores. Publicly, she rejoices at each of her children's successes, even as she winces when she sees the pain in her sick son's eyes as he sees his brother and sisters gradually achieve everything he ever wanted. Joy goes away and cries in private. There can come a point when your child has been more hurt than you can bear.

It may help if you find yourself in Joy's situation to admit to such feelings and recognize why you are having them. They are natural and do not for one moment suggest that other members of the family have suddenly become unimportant.

Nevertheless, all members of the family have their own needs and fulfilling them will not in any way affect the chances of the sufferer eventually finding a way forward. It is important that the joys and successes of each should be celebrated in that context. Life is short for all of us and none of us know what tomorrow will bring for ourselves or for any of those we love, so it is important that we should rejoice in each and every good thing that happens to ourselves and them without feelings of guilt. If you find you are unable to do this, then there may be further regrets and remorse waiting for you in the future. Don't forget, it can also help to be positive about any successes achieved by the sufferer as well, and, no matter how small, to celebrate these.

A reaction to a successful recovery

Rather differently, you may be spared, like Edna, the agonies of watching your child suffer the more severe and long-term effects of this type of illness.

Edna
She watched her son gradually pick up the pieces of his life, eventually return to college and come out triumphantly at the end of the course. Edna was justly proud and grateful for this. However, she used to wake up in a cold sweat some nights, quaking with fear that this same son could lose everything he had so painstakingly achieved, that it could all happen again.

She felt ashamed about this, knowing she had no right to fret when her son had been spared, when he had been so lucky compared with several others she knows whose lives have been wrecked by their illness. She realises only too well how their mothers must envy her and what they would give to see their son or daughter do so well. So, she wondered, how could she be so selfish, so inadequate?

The answer is very simple. She has been there, has faced the same dread as these other mothers and knows that it could have happened to her son and that he will, anyway, always be vulnerable now. During the day, she rejoices in his success and newly regained happiness and can believe, with justification, that it will last. But, at night, her fears return.

Edna has no reason to feel guilty, inadequate or ungrateful, her son's success hasn't deprived others of their health – indeed, she would be so happy to share her good fortune with other mothers if she could! It is not ungrateful to be afraid – it is all part of loving someone and then suddenly finding them to be so much at risk.

131

Time will help relieve these feelings, but it will never completely erase Edna's moments of doubt. Meanwhile, I was able to help her to channel such anxieties into quietly determining to be positive while remaining unobstrusively vigilant and watchful in case the time should ever come when her son seems vulnerable and in need of a friend.

A reaction to the effects of a chronic illness

What about a less fortunate mother? In Chapter 6, we noted Marian's feelings of guilt whenever she acknowledges the 15 years of unresolved bereavement she has felt since her son Jeff was struck down with a damaging schizophrenic illness, but something else bothered her, too.

Marian
Even more painful to her was the unresolved anger she used to feel about his behaviour when her father died suddenly and without warning. Her first reaction was to fret about how his death would affect her son as he and his grandfather had spent so many happy hours together before Jeff's illness. They had been such pals, they had been two of a kind! To his family's amazement, Jeff shrugged and smiled when he heard the news and showed no other reaction at that time or later. Neither did he respond in any way to his mother's distress over the loss of her father nor go to the funeral.

If your relative suffers from all the negative symptoms of a chronic schizophrenic illness, then you may appreciate only too well why this phenomenon we call 'blunted emotion' tends to alienate and distance sufferers from their families more than any other feature of schizophrenia. At worst, relatives see this apparent indifference as some sort of callousness. At best, they may come to believe that they and others do not matter any more.

Textbooks on schizophrenia tend to confirm that there is a loss of feeling or concern for others – sufferers becoming totally absorbed in their inner world and what is happening to them. My experience is reassuringly different.

Over the years, I have seen some very moving examples of caring among chronic schizophrenia sufferers and have gradually come to realise that these have only been evident in certain special conditions, situations in which there is no question of being embarrassed over their attempts to involve themselves in another's distress and where they appreciate that no one else is available, or able, to intervene. In other words, these feelings will only come out – will only find an expression –

on occasions when there is no expectation of a certain type of social behaviour, such as you find, for example, during a family tragedy or at a funeral.

In case this blunted emotion causes pain and distress in your family, let me explain. When Marian talked to me about her family's hurt and anger, I told her what I believed was happening in that situation. We are looking at individuals who have to cope with a cluster of negative symptoms, (described in Chapter 2). First, you will recall sufferers complain of feelings of 'flatness' instead of the ups and downs – the joys and the sadness – that the rest of us experience. This means they cannot react at the emotional level that, in the rest of us, releases our inhibitions and enables us to stretch out to others in times of trouble or great happiness.

Second, they are profoundly inhibited by a poverty of speech and an inability to initiate and make conversation or, even more to the point, to say what might be expected of them.

Third, we know that this poverty of speech is associated with a little-understood influence that this illness has on *expression* as well as speech.

Finally, and not surprisingly, these difficulties associated with reaching out to others and reacting spontaneously escalate an existing heightened self-consciousness. Is it any wonder, then, that the individual retreats from emotional situations?

When Marian thought about this, she was able to recognize occasions in her own life – usually in rather formal situations – when she, too, has been able to do little more than shrug and smile, although she knew this to be inappropriate, that more might be expected of her. She has also come to realise since the time we first spoke about it that Jeff has, in fact, found ways to stretch out to comfort her – with a touch or a smile or a cup of tea and toast when she has been ill in bed – and she knows this has been when there were no social demands he couldn't fulfill and when no one else was there to help her at those times.

We were both glad that Marian had been able to express her anger and, thus, eventually resolve it, making life a little more rewarding for her and her son.

Martyrdom – delegated rather than voluntary!

When an illness turns out to be very incapacitating, there is a pronounced tendency for society to leave it to the family, to the carers – or, more often, a sole carer – to get on with it. I have met too many of them over the years who do just that without thanks from the hard-pressed mental health services and, very often, without the funds that would make life just that little bit easier for them. They are even exhorted by 'the experts' not to make martyrs of themselves and, in the circumstances, this might be more than just a little galling!

As you will know if all this is very familiar to you, one of the worrying aspects of this sort of situation is that sufferer and carer can be locked in an unhealthy relationship because there is no escape, no respite from each other's company. Both can feel trapped – one by incapacity and the other by a duty, however caring they are – and this sort of frustration may override all that is potentially positive in the relationship.

It is very important that both parties should be kind to themselves. These reactions are normal and you should lose no time in seeking ways, perhaps with the help of the local mental health services, to rescue the relationship. This is not likely to happen unless both sufferer and carer have a chance to find some stimulation outside of the home and some space and privacy within the home. It might also help both of you to have someone to moan to about things, if the third party truly understands the reasons for this and doesn't leave you feeling guilty and disloyal! Also it may be very relevant to consider taking advantage of recent legislation, which allows for carers to have their *own* needs assessed by local authorities when the *sufferer's* needs are being assessed. One resource gradually becoming more widely available is respite care, which can enable a lone carer to have a few hours out of the home each week to go shopping, visit a friend or whatever or to allow parents, perhaps almost housebound by their role as carers, to have an opportunity to go away for an occasional holiday together.

If you gasped just now at the idea of being able to go out shopping on your own or to visit a friend or to get away for a holiday, then go for it and seek an assessment and find out what might be available locally for you and others of that special band of unsung heroes whose caring means they are taxed beyond the call of duty.

Perhaps it might be a good idea for both sufferer *and* carer to suggest to professionals who come to do these assessments that each of their own needs might be better met if the other could be enabled to enjoy a more rewarding lifestyle?

The pain of embarrassment

A serious mental illness can cause embarrassment to everyone in the family. In many cases, this will only be the case during a first episode, but, in others, this may recur with later relapses.

It is natural to feel exposed and betrayed by abnormal behaviour in one's family. We can all feel mortified by behaviour that singles us out in front of friends or strangers and obvious examples of this can be a manic father or brother grabbing hold of acquaintances in the street and excitedly bombarding them with unrealistic ideas and plans or a schizophrenic mother or daughter with delusional ideas, accusing the neighbours of radiating poisonous gas into her bedroom.

If you are a young person, then this sort of experience may make you very angry and hurt. It can be difficult to cope with such anger, particularly as this may make you feel you are being selfish or disloyal as well. Such feelings are natural, though, and it is important that you should feel able to talk about them, either with other family members or, perhaps, with a family friend or a teacher you feel able to confide in.

Once the illness has been diagnosed, it may be that the family will meet others who have been there, too, and so understand what it feels like.

You may also find out more about the illness and how it feels to suffer from it. All of this can help to make things easier and, incidentally, to completely remove any ideas you may have had about you or anyone else being in some way responsible for what has happened.

If your relative's responses or behaviour continue to embarrass you, whatever your age, then you may tend to avoid inviting friends to the house. This, too, is natural, but it is worth bearing in mind that trusted friends may be far more tolerant than you expect, particularly if you feel able to share with them some information about how the illness feels for the sufferer. This can bring the bonus of an additional source of comfort and support if and when you need it.

On a refreshingly reassuring note, one MD sufferer I know has pointed out that when she was ill, a source of embarrassment for the husband was her conviction that she was Jesus Christ. Later, when she was well again, it became an embarrassment for her, too, when she realised that some of the couple's closest friends knew about this because she had tried to recruit them as her disciples! It is a source of pleasure to her now that if Jesus or God are mentioned when she and her husband are out with friends, then it becomes a big joke that she can enjoy with them all.

Can it happen to me?

Again, if you are the brother or sister or daughter or son of a sufferer and are old enough to worry about it, you will almost certainly be asking yourself, 'Can this happen to me?' You may well feel unable to ask such a question of your family and not know who else to turn to.

135

As this can be a very real source of fear and anxiety for many relatives, it may help you to know that no one can answer this question with a 'yes' or 'no' for *anyone*. Two in every hundred of the population will suffer from MD or schizophrenia at some time in their lives and we don't know *which* two they will be! However, there are certain factors that make it rather more likely, such as having two parents who are sufferers or several blood relatives or an identical twin. Even in the latter case (where the odds are heaviest, because these twins share identical genes), there is less than a 50 per cent chance that the identical twin of a schizophrenia sufferer will also develop the illness. More importantly, over half of all cases don't even run in families as far as we can tell and your relative may well have developed such an illness for reasons we don't understand at the present time.

Beyond being sensible about any symptoms you might have in the future and seeking help at once if you are at all anxious – in the same way that you would about any unexplained *physical* aches or pains – and being very careful to avoid taking unnecessary risks, such as abusing street drugs or alcohol, then the message has to be 'don't make yourself ill worrying about something that will probably never happen!'

Feelings of abuse – the effects of paranoia

It can be deeply hurtful to have someone you love and respect come to loathe and distrust you, albeit only temporarily and at times of breakdown. You may ask yourself, 'Where have I gone wrong?'

Quite apart from the pain of being distrusted, the sufferer may also really believe at such times that you have done, or wished to do, appalling things. On top of this, you may then find that these ideas have been shared with others who, not appreciating this is madness, take the attitude that 'there is no smoke without a fire!'

As you may know from personal experience, the victims of such paranoid ideas may wonder if they are to come out of such a situation with any dignity or credibility and, not surprisingly, they may find they feel very angry as well as hurt.

It helps to keep a sense of proportion on the lines of 'well, people will believe what they want to', but it can be disconcerting nevertheless! If at all possible, the only real way to deal with this situation is to keep reminding oneself that it is the *illness* that is at fault, not your relative and not yourself. Also, far from being caused by something you have done wrong, paranoia in psychosis unfailingly focuses on those who matter most to the sufferer.

136

In time, you both may be able to laugh with friends about ideas that were based on delusional thinking rather than on facts. Indeed, this happened with Jane's family, as we noted in Chapter 10. Perhaps it is not surprising that they have not been able to reconcile themselves to this betrayal, as they see it, by 'caring' professionals, nor have they been able to quieten their fears that it could all happen again. Nevertheless, Jane and her parents share these misgivings and they have not allowed what happened to affect their relationships with each other.

Perhaps this brings us back to where we started – with each member of the family finding a way through to a life after a serious mental illness.

14

Surviving a serious mental illness

Much of this book has focused on sufferers who have the close support of a family. At the time of a first episode of a serious mental illness this can be vitally important and it may continue to be so if an illness becomes persistent and debilitating. However, for most sufferers, this sort of intensive support becomes less crucial as time goes on and some may eventually choose to live independently and, perhaps, to go on to make equally important new relationships. Although this has long been the normal pattern for any family, things have been changing in recent years. Significantly high unemployment, together with a scarcity of available housing, have made it increasingly difficult for young people to move on and set up home for themselves.

To move or not to move?

It is worth keeping this in mind if you are one of those sufferers who feel you should be moving on but have little real incentive to do this as you like having familiar faces around you and also realise that living as part of the family may be less complicated and cheaper than living on your own. These are good reasons – and there are others – for thinking hard before making a decision to move out of the family home. If you are happy where you are and pulling your weight (as much as the next one, anyway!) and everyone seems happy for you to be there (at least most of the time anway), then think on it! Many families are quite content for a member who might be vulnerable to stay within the nest and yours may well be one of these.

If, on the other hand, you are eager to move on and have carefully considered the options and all the everyday practical issues involved with living independently, then this too can work very well for some sufferers, particularly if the new situation does not lead to being alone too much of the time. Whatever you do, try to keep up family ties if these have been rewarding in the past and make a point of inviting yourself for a regular meal particularly at times when you're waiting for the next giro or pay cheque. Most families do expect and welcome this, you know!

Well, let's assume that you have now reached the stage where you can make choices about this and other aspects of your life and, perhaps, about the more distant future.

Employment or some other occupation

Your health and a certain amount of luck will probably dictate whether or not you are gainfully employed. Given that you find your work reasonably stimulating and unstressful, then this is likely to be a big plus in your life and, hopefully, financially rewarding as well. If, however, work seems to be out of the question – for the time being, anyway – then you have probably found that it is important for you to be occupied most days, with a routine that minimises boredom and periods of restlessness.

It may be that you will choose, or continue, to attend a day centre or do some studying or voluntary work or a mix of any of these. Increasingly, sufferers are getting involved in helping with the running of resources such as 'drop in' centres where they attend as clients. A few are taking up new careers in the self-help movement, perhaps campaigning for better services and treatment for those with a serious mental illness. What really matters is that you find a way of life that suits you and which maximises your chances to fulfil your potential to have a rewarding life.

I have noted in the past that one snag for some sufferers who are not working, but are nevertheless content with their lifestyle, is not being sure what to answer when asked by a stranger in a pub 'and what work do you do?' With time, we found that several answers served very well, such as 'I'm waiting for the job situation to improve' or 'I used to do . . . but I'm out of work at present' or 'I'm doing a bit of studying at the moment'. As you may have discovered for yourself, people are not wanting precise details but, rather, a conversation starter and some common ground to chat about. It is a pity to worry too much about one's lifestyle. So many people are unemployed these days that this need not be a social hindrance except, of course, when it restricts one's spending power – and that's another common problem!

What to tell about the illness

The above example of 'What should I say?' brings us to the thorny question of what to tell others about your illness. For some sufferers, and especially those who have a job and a very normal lifestyle, the answer may be, quite simply, nothing. For others, the matter may be more complicated. If you have friends, neighbours and the like who wonder why you don't work, then you may want to tell them about your illness and how it affects you (or not as the case may be).

You will almost certainly find that it is a case of balancing certain issues against others. For example, do you spend a lot of your time with other sufferers or old friends who accept you for what you are? Or are you someone for whom coming out about it, as it were, may affect future chances of employment, choice of companions and the chance to get to know members of the opposite sex whom you may be attracted to.

Such a decision has to be a personal one. Most of the individuals I have known have chosen something between the two, gradually sharing certain amounts of information with some of their contacts until such time as they have felt relaxed about telling them more. I certainly wouldn't recommend Ray's approach when he met two attractive girls in a pub and sat with them for an hour or so before announcing pleasantly Oh, yes, I know all about nerves, too – I'm a schizophrenic'. He then went off to the loo and was actually surprised to find the table empty when he returned! He had a good laugh with the group when he reported this first attempt at 'coming out' and promptly improved on this approach to the point where he's been happily settled with his partner for several years.

Telling those who matter

This brings us to an even more important dilemma – how to tell *those who matter* about what has happened to you. You may already have had to face this problem or are very much aware that one day you will have to. You will most certainly have realised that you cannot hope to prove you really love someone by denying what has happened to you.

This is appallingly difficult for many sufferers, but it all eventually comes down to trust. Although it is very tempting, it is neither fair nor reasonable to hide the truth from someone you wish to spend much of the rest of your life with. That person has to be given a choice about something so potentially important. Equally, if you don't tell, then a relapse at a later date might cost you a loved one's support just when you are especially vulnerable.

Though all this is true, it can, nevertheless, be a heart-rending decision to make as it may be that the cost will seem too high and your prospective partner may not be able to cope with the sort of risk that may be inherent in your having such an illness. Perhaps his or her family will intervene and succeed in ending the relationship. On the other hand, some relationships have gone on to survive and flourish once prospective partners have come to terms with the facts.

In deciding how to go about sharing information with someone very important to you, a 'softly, softly' approach makes considerably more sense than Ray's approach! There is no need, nor is it advisable, to launch in to explanations at the beginning of a friendship and, later, a gradual sharing of the facts can be helpful and easier to accept. One potentially important matter in a heterosexual relationship that may need airing along the way is whether or not either partner wants to have children and this in itself may lead on to discussing the 'ins and outs' of a serious mental illness.

Genetic counselling

This may be available at the Maudsley Hospital in South London for couples wishing to explore the possibility of starting a family and wanting to know about any known genetic risks. We touched on these briefly in Chapter 1 and again in Chapter 13, and it may suffice for now to note that there is more chance of contracting MD or schizophrenia if one has a close relative with the illness and the risk may increase two or three times if both parents have a serious mental illness.

I tend to advise those who ask me about this that it is equally important to consider the potential mother's own health, stability and levels of energy if she is a sufferer. Will these be adequate to the task of coping with all the needs and demands of a baby and, later, a small child, on a day-to-day basis? This can be a mammoth challenge for even the fittest of mothers. Much may depend also on the ready availability of one's partner and other family members to help out along the way.

Pregnancy

There is a further matter that calls for careful consideration. It is likely that mothers-to-be will need to come off their medication. The Manic Depression Fellowship provides a leaflet on pregnancy and medication for MD sufferers and the National Schizophrenia Fellowship Advice Line or SANELINE should be able to offer advice on this subject for other sufferers (see the Useful addresses section at the back of the book).

If you are dependent on your medication to keep well and you are considering pregnancy, then it is important that you discuss this very carefully with doctors and obtain a promise of ongoing support from them if you go ahead with starting a family. It is essential that all sides of the question are considered beforehand, including a possible need to take medication at some time during the pregnancy. It might be an excellent idea to compile an Advance Directive (as discussed in Chapter 4) about what you would want to happen if you became vulnerable. Neither the baby nor you will be well served if you become severely psychotic while pregnant and it can and does happen.

Childbirth

Similarly, everyone needs to be aware that there may be a risk of relapse following childbirth, although this is by no means necessarily the case. Also, the baby will probably need to be bottle-fed as many mothers will need to resume at least a maintenance dose of medication after the birth and the drug could otherwise be passed to the baby in the mother's milk.

Deciding for or against

After all these warnings, it is only fair to say that it will be right and safe for some female sufferers to start a family and you may well be one of them. Just be fair to yourself and remember when making a decision that your first consideration should be to maximize your chances of staying well.

If you decide to go ahead, then do take note of my firm recommendation that you obtain a promise of ongoing support from doctors throughout your pregnancy. That done, you can then concentrate all your efforts on taking care of yourself and the baby and enjoying motherhood!

Keeping well

And that brings us to the important matter of each and every sufferer finding ways to enjoy life and to maximize their chances of staying well.

In this book I have focused several times on the precariousness of trusting the system to successfully look after your health. 'Too little, too late' might well describe the deal that many sufferers and families receive from the mental health services. The good news, however, is that, as we have seen, this service may now be complimented by self-management programmes like those pioneered by sufferers in the United States and which are now being promoted by members of the Manic Depression Fellowship in this country.

The most positive aspect of self-management is that sufferers choose to take responsibility for their own health and for keeping well and that this is achieved by health professionals, family and friends working in partnership with them. For the first time, sufferers stand to have an important say in their own treatment and formulating their own 'keeping well' strategies while benefiting from the various skills, medicines and support networks that these call for and others can provide. Perhaps most important of all, sufferers can start to make choices and optimize their own survival skills along the way.

How does this sound to you? If you are not already involved in a self-management programme, where would you start in your own case? Perhaps with the thorny subject of medication?

The pros and cons of medication

Because we tend to regard drugs as intrusive, many of us are reluctant to take them unless we know what they are meant to do and we can see that they achieve this. This becomes problematic when we are talking about psychosis as, by definition, this can mar the individual's reasoning over such matters! Furthermore, if you feel good – and are, in fact, keeping well – then this may seem to be another sound reason for not bothering with medication. All this means that individuals with a serious mental illness may see no need to take medicatiaon when they are well or when they are relapsing. Add to this the fact that many will have trying side-effects from the drugs – particularly on starting them, but, in some cases, for much of the time. It is not surprising, then, that 'non-compliance with treatment', as doctors call it, is not uncommon.

Despite this, as you may know, many sufferers *do* come to terms with their medication and some very well individuals swear by it as the only means by which they can keep their psychosis at bay. They may be the lucky ones for more than one reason. Often they are the individuals whom professionals have listened to when they have complained of some intolerable side-effect, whose doctors have gone to considerable effort to find the right drug and dose for them and whose progress on medication has been carefully monitored. It is worth bearing in mind that these are not part of that tiny minority of individuals who have just one episode of a serious mental illness and who don't seem to need medication after a while – they are sufferers who keep really well if they keep taking their medication but relapse if they come off it.

Life is not so simple for those who feel they have not had this sort of treatment or who do not respond well to the currently available drugs. If you are one of these, it might be a good idea to consider taking this up in a positive way with the professionals involved to find out if there have been any advances in medication that you are not aware of and if there are any new ways in which to deal with any side-effects you may suffer from. It may be that you would then feel better placed to influence which options are best in your case in the future and it may be that you could benefit sooner rather than later from new research as there are various new drugs on the horizon.

The reason, of course, that many sufferers settle for taking maintenance medication in the end is that the alternatives can be so devastating. It all seems to come down to comparing the hassle of taking medication regularly, together with any side-effects and perceived risks, with the long catalogue of disasters (listed at the beginning of Chapter 10) associated with an unresolved psychotic illness.

This is where the fine balance comes in, but it may be very much easier for you to appreciate this if you are given the opportunities to discuss it and make informed choices. For obvious reasons, we all tend to do better in situations we have chosen rather than those that have been imposed upon us, and few can be more important than this aspect of coping with a serious mental illness.

Other components of a 'keeping well' programme

We have already looked at various ways that may help you to protect yourself from relapse. Some of these are concerned with taking up a lifestyle that particularly suits you and, of course, avoiding factors that can make you more vulnerable. In the first category, this may include finding a rewarding way to spend your day – an occupation, albeit paid or unpaid, amenable company and a social network that includes individuals who will keep an eye on you and discuss any signs of trouble you may not have noticed yourself. Perhaps most important of all, it will involve knowing one's own vulnerability and the first warning signs of a return of unwanted symptoms. In the second category, many individuals will be put at risk by drug or alcohol abuse – some to the point where they put themselves beyond help if they persevere with the habit. Others, particularly sufferers with a chronic schizophrenic illness, need to be protected from unnecessary changes in their daily lives as they can find these very threatening. Some individuals will need to avoid situations that can involve extremes of excitement – highs brought about by appearing successfully in public, for example, or even by heated debates that seem to be enjoyable at the time. At the other end of the extreme, too much inactivity and understimulation can be unproductive and flattening, even intolerable for some. Another fine balance needs to be achieved here, too!

MD sufferers may need to make arrangements to hand over any belongings that give them access to reckless spending, or other excesses, if they feel their mood is lifting too much. Ideally, they should have some trusted soul who can take over any spare cash, credit cards, building society books and car keys until the scare is over. Some find it helps to cancel any dates and other appointments and to avoid the telephone – to lie low.

Finally, a piece of advice which one well-recovered schizophrenia sufferer always gives to others struggling after a breakdown, which is to keep a diary and compare your progress with that of six months ago. Sometimes the improvements can be so gradual that they can be missed unless they are seen in these real terms. Some MD sufferers also advocate writing about themselves and what is happening on a daily basis. You may find this can be both therapeutic and helpful in gaining a better understanding of yourself.

Serious mental illness – a family affair

Well, we seem to have come full circle and, in this last chapter, have extolled the virtues and strengths of sufferers going on to make their way within a supportive social network and perhaps with the help of a self-management programme. In many cases, this social network may include their close relatives and everyone in the family will come to realise that they have, in fact, survived a serious mental illness.

For some, this survival will be literally that and there will be little to celebrate, except that a loved one has received what help and protection you could provide. For others, it will be real cause for celebration. For all those families in between, in which there will be bad as well as good times, take heart. You have done your best and you have survived!

Further Reading

Amis, Kingsley, *Stanley and the Women*, Penguin, 1989.

Vintage Kingsley Amis, with his usual brand of wit and cynicism, this is a gem of a book. It is a brilliant take-off of the sorts of things that can happen to those families who are unfortunate enough to find themselves grappling with ill-informed professionals as well as with a serious mental illness!

Copeland, Mary Ellen, *The Depression Workshop: A guide for living with depression*, New Harbinger Publications Incorporated, 1992.

A beautifully presented and useful 'working manual', packed full of ideas, exercises and projects that help to better cope with and protect oneself from a depressive illness.

Copeland, Mary Ellen, *Living with depression and manic depression*, New Harbinger Publications Incorporated, 1994.

This is an inspiring book by an MD sufferer and campaigner and outlines a self-management programme approach, including the recruiting and appointing of named persons to support and represent the individual and the use of advance directives, all bringing a new meaning to the words 'self-determination'.

Department of Health and Welsh Office *Code of Practice: Mental Health Act 1983*, HMSO, 1993, available from HMSO and some booksellers from PO Box 276, London SW8 5DT (tel. 0171–873 9090).

This book provides useful information on the law and an excellent insight into currently recommended professional practice. Highly recommended for information and reference purposes for families.

Disability Alliance, *Disability Rights Handbook*, available from Disability Alliance, 1st Floor East, Universal House, 88/94 Wentworth Street, London E1 7SA (tel: 0171–247 8776).

Excellent and comprehensive handbook, updated at the beginning of each financial year, on benefits and allowances for the disabled.

Howe, Gwen, *Schizophrenia: A fresh approach*, David & Charles, 2nd edition, 1990.

A useful introduction to schizophrenia, written by myself, with detailed discussion on a dietary approach to schizophrenia where abnormal cravings and bingeing are a feature of the illness. No longer in print, but available in public libraries and also from the Schizophrenia Association of Great Britain and the National Schizophrenia Fellowship (see the Useful addresses section for their addresses).

Howe, Gwen, *The Reality of Schizophrenia*, Faber & Faber, 1991.

This book covers all the usual aspects of living with schizophrenia and attempts to explain the history and perspective of the ideology and politics surrounding it and their irrelevance to the everyday problems of having to live with a serious mental illness.

Howe, Gwen, *Working with Schizophrenia*, Jessica Kingsley, 1995

This book was written by myself together with the help of 12 sufferers and carers, and several professional colleagues. It introduces a tried and tested needs-based approach to working with schizophrenia. Primarily written for professionals, both the Foreword and reviews from members of self-help organisations have also recommended it for sufferers and families.

Moate, Mary, and Enoch, David, *Schizophrenia: Voices in the dark*, Kingsway Publications, Eastbourne, East Sussex, 1990.

A Christian sufferer has written 'much fear and guilt is evident and breakdown can be interpreted as failure to be a good Christian'. She feels this book has much to offer all those in the Church trying to grapple with this dilemma. A good introduction to the subject with a compassionate contribution by a mother of a schizophrenic son and a psychiatrist who has worked with this type of illness for many years.

North, Carol, *Welcome Silence*, Simon and Schuster, 1988.

An illuminating 'blow-by-blow' account of this American woman's struggle with constant voices while she was at medical college. She went on to become a psychiatrist and decided to share her personal experiences of a psychotic illness.

Finally, two exciting new publications from The Manic Depression Fellowship (see the Useful addresses section next for their address):

Inside Out, produced and published by the Manic Depression Fellowship, 1995.
- A guide to the self-management of MD.

Outside In, produced and published by the Manic Depression Fellowship, 1997.
A guide to self-management for the relatives and friends of those who experience manic depressive episodes.

Useful addresses

Manic Depression Fellowship (MDF)
8–10 High Street
Kingston upon Thames
Surrey KT1 1EY
0181–974 6550

Offers advice and support to those having to cope with a manic
depressive illness, together with open meetings and local self-help
groups. Also involved in campaigning and promoting better services.
Produces the excellent quarterly journal, *Pendulum.*

National Schizophrenia Fellowship (NSF)
18 Castle Street
Kingston-upon-Thames
Surrey KT1 1SS
0181–547 3937

Concerned with helping all those affected by a serious mental illness,
and with improving services and promoting education and knowledge.
Also increasingly a service provider. Regular newsletters and conferences. Local self-help groups throughout the country. Addresses and
telephone numbers of regional offices can be obtained from their head
office.

Highly recommended advice and support service from the NSF Advice
Line: 0181–974 6814 (open 10 am–3 pm weekdays)

SANE (Schizophrenia a National Emergency)
199–205 Old Marylebone Road
London NW1 5QP
0171–724 6520

Now concerned with research, campaigning and promoting knowledge
about all serious mental illness. Occasional newsletters.

SANE Helpline: 0171–724 8000 (open afternoons, evenings and
weekends)

Schizophrenia Association of Great Britain (SAGB)
International Schizophrenia Centre
Bryn Hyfryd
The Crescent
Bangor,
Gwynedd LL57 2AG
01248 354048

Concerned with helping those having to cope with a schizophrenic illness. Involved in research and campaigning. Produces a newsletter.

The ZITO Trust
PO Box 265
London WC2H 9JD
0171–240 2326

Concerned with the advocating for the victims of the failure of Community Care policy and compaigning for better services for the severely mentally ill whose condition can pose a threat to themselves and to others.

Depression Alliance
309 The Chandlery
50 Westminister Bridge Road
London SE1 7QY
0171–721 7411

Index

151